W9-CRS-201

Merry Christmas —
To Bob
From Mother & D. OB
12 – 1991

Decline and Fail

Decline and Fail

The
Ailing
Nuclear Power
Industry

Peter Stoler

Dodd, Mead & Company

New York

Copyright © 1985 by Peter Stoler

All rights reserved
No part of this book may be reproduced in any form
without permission in writing from the publisher.

Published by Dodd, Mead & Company, Inc.
79 Madison Avenue, New York, N.Y. 10016
Distributed in Canada by
McClelland and Stewart Limited, Toronto

Manufactured in the United States of America
Designed by Tom Mellers
First Edition

Library of Congress Cataloging in Publication Data

Stoler, Peter.
  Decline and fail.

  Bibliography: p.
  Includes index.
  1. Nuclear industry—United States. 2. Electric
utilities—United States. I. Title.
HD9698.U52S8 1985   338.4'762148'0973   84-28607
ISBN 0-396-08527-X

For my parents, who knew that I wanted to write, encouraged me, and never, not even once, asked me what I was going to do to make a living.

Contents

One   The Critical Mass   *1*

Two   In the Beginning . . .   *16*

Three   The Troubled Childhood   *39*

Four   A Difficult Adolescence   *57*

Five   No Business Like Nuke Business   *78*

Six   A Rude Awakening   *95*

Seven   The Reasons Why   *117*

Eight   Storm Warnings   *134*

Nine   The Crash of '84   *152*

Ten   Energy for the Future   *166*

Source Notes   *183*

Bibliography   *190*

Index   *192*

Decline and Fail

One

The Critical Mass

> **DIED.** The U.S. nuclear power industry, 27, onetime hope of American energy consumers and utility companies; of environmental opposition and obstruction, governmental interference, lack of public confidence and self-inflicted injuries due to bad judgment, poor management and insensitivity; in Washington, D.C., and in the states of Pennsylvania, Washington, Indiana and Ohio. A child of the Manhattan Project, the industry attempted to harness the atom for peace, but failed to live down its lethal image.

This obituary notice has not yet appeared in the "Milestones" column of *Time* magazine. Similar notices have yet to be printed in the pages of *The New York Times* or other newspapers. But there are many Americans who would be glad to read them. Opponents and critics of nuclear power have, in fact, been hoping for years to see just such announcements. Many are prepared to see them written today. Most are just as ready to stand dry-eyed at the graveside

1

and watch the industry's interment, and equally willing to remain after the service to toss a few shovelfuls of earth into the grave. Some, indeed, feel that the obituary is overdue and argue that the industry is already dead. As far as they are concerned, the nuclear power industry need only be informed of its death so that it can lie down or at least cooperate with the burial party.

Those who feel that the nuclear power industry is dead are wrong. But the nuclear power industry is ailing. It is sicker than many of its members are willing to concede. Its condition, which has never been all that robust recently, has taken a number of turns for the worse during the past decade. Faced with a patient in similar condition, a doctor might either give up or resort to heroic measures to keep him alive. With his ship in the same state, even a skilled skipper might be forgiven for taking to the lifeboats, or at least ordering them swung out and made ready.

Few question that the U.S. nuclear power industry is in critical condition. But as Mark Twain once observed in a slightly different context, reports of its death are premature. The worst fears of its proponents, the worst wishes of its opponents notwithstanding, the U.S. nuclear power industry is still alive.

But not well. Like a patient with a serious disease, the industry has weathered several crises over the past decade. And each of these crises has eroded its strength, left it gravely weakened. The next crisis, no matter how serious it may be, may not kill it. But it could seal its fate and leave it too weak to recover, like a patient whose illness has passed the point of no return and whose condition can only deteriorate until death ends its decline.

For the simple fact is that the U.S. nuclear industry is dying. Orders for new nuclear power plants, at least from U.S. utility companies, stopped coming in in the late seventies. No American utility has placed an order for a new nuclear power plant since 1978. Cancellation of orders has become commonplace. A total of eighteen orders was canceled in 1982. In 1984 at least half a dozen plants, some of them all but completed, were abandoned as utilities realized, not without a certain amount of pain and not without a definite loss of pride, that it was more economical to let these giants sit unused and incomplete, like ruined castles, than it was to try to finish and operate them.[1]

Across the country, from Pennsylvania to Washington, from Michigan to Alabama, nuclear plants in various stages of construction sit gaunt against the sky, like cities whose inhabitants have fled, like Troys awaiting discovery by some modern-day Schliemann. In Illinois, Commonwealth Edison's new Byron 1 plant, nearly complete at a cost of $3.7 billion, is sitting idle. In an unprecedented move, the Nuclear Regulatory Commission, the federal agency charged with licensing and regulating nuclear plants, announced early in 1984 that it had "no confidence" in the quality-control procedures used during the plant's construction. Therefore, it said, it would do something that had never been done before in the history of nuclear power in the U.S. It would deny the company a license to operate the plant.

The NRC's decision not to license Byron shook the nuclear industry, which had come to consider the granting of a license a formality, something that it was required to request but something whose issuance it could take for granted. But it was hardly the only setback suffered by the nuclear industry in the opening months of 1984. Before industry leaders could fully absorb the impact of the NRC action against Byron, they were struck another blow. Indiana's Public Service Company announced that it was canceling all further work on its 2,260-megawatt Marble Hill plant, half completed at a cost of some $2.5 billion. The decision put a severe strain on the company's finances. In making its announcement, Public Service said that it would have to eliminate one hundred jobs and put more than five hundred of the utility's remaining four thousand workers on a four-day week.

A few days later, another blow rocked the shaken nuclear power industry. Cincinnati Gas and Electric and two partner companies announced that they were halting further construction on their long-troubled William H. Zimmer plant. Worse, from the industry's point of view, Cincinnati Gas and Electric announced that it was thinking of going over to the opposition. Company officials disclosed that they were looking into the feasibility, both economic and technical, of converting the 1,100-megawatt plant, 97 percent complete at a cost exceeding $3.1 billion, from a nuclear to a coal-fired facility, thus giving at least a moral boost to those who had been insisting that coal was preferable to the atom as a source of electric power.

The industry had barely absorbed this news when a fourth blow fell. The Philadelphia Electric Company agreed to a demand by the Pennsylvania state public utilities commission that it stanch its financial hemorrhaging. Reluctantly, it agreed to halt construction on one of its two Limerick reactors, on which it had already spent at least $3.3 billion, for at least eighteen months.

The cancellations of 1984 could not have come at a worse time for the nuclear power industry. Industry leaders had been watching anxiously as the 1983 economic recovery had begun to nudge the demand for electricity slowly upward. They had begun to express cautious optimism that nuclear plants, which had generated more than 300 billion kilowatts, or 13 percent of the nation's electricity, in 1983, could further increase their role in the country's electric power game.[2]

The cancellations also produced an undeniable sense of satisfaction among atomic energy's opponents. Her male colleagues at the Illinois antinuclear group known as Business and Professional People for the Public Interest were so elated by the NRC's decision on Commonwealth Edison's Byron 1 plant that they picked up Jane Wicher, a 105-pound lawyer who had led the fight against the plant's construction, and carried her around the office on their shoulders. "It was an extremely important ruling," she said. "It has an impact far beyond Byron. It sends the message to the utilities that they cannot take the issuance of an operating license for granted. That's a message the utilities have never heard before." Melody Moore, director of the Chicago-based group Citizens Against Nuclear Power, expressed similar sentiments. "What we are seeing is a domino effect," she said. "It's getting into billions and billions of dollars and it's all coming out of the rate payers' pockets. This is a failed technology."[3]

Others went even further and described the events of early 1984 as the beginning of the end for the American nuclear power industry. "Nuclear power has been walking around like Dracula for the last few years," said a young man who answered the telephone at the San Francisco headquarters of the Sierra Club, one of the nation's leading environmentalist organizations. "These cancellations are the stake through his heart."[4] Other environmentalists said that they hoped his statement was accurate while declining to go quite so far on their own. But one leading industrialist was willing to at least let the referee start counting nuclear power out. "It's well into free fall," said John Nichols, chairman of Illinois Tool Works, of the battered industry. "It's beyond recovery."[5]

Spokesmen for the nuclear power industry conceded that it was in trouble; no one attempted to deny, in fact, that it was in serious trouble. Carl Walske, president of the industry organization known as the Atomic Industrial Forum, refused, however, to strike his flag. "We're still here," said Walske in the wake of the 1984 cancellations. "We plan to be here for a long time."

In remarks that reminded even sympathetic listeners of a man whistling past a graveyard, Walske insisted that things were not quite as bad as they looked for nuclear power. He insisted, for example, that nuclear power was still a factor in U.S. electricity production, and his recitation of the facts made it clear that, in fact, it was. At the beginning of 1984, U.S. utilities had at least eighty nuclear power plants, from small installations like the Yankee Atomic Electric Company's 175-megawatt* plant at Rowe, Massachusetts, to the Tennessee Valley Authority's two 1,148-megawatt Sequoyah plants in Daisy, Tennessee, on-line and producing electricity. The total of 300 billion kilowatts these plants produced in 1983 represented a healthy 9.5 percent increase over the power produced by the atom in 1982 and a better performance than that turned in by the utility industry as a whole.

Nor, as Walske was quick to point out in reviewing 1983's events, was the year a bad one for nuclear power in other respects. Nineteen eighty-three saw four new nuclear power plants authorized to operate, bringing to seventeen the number of plants approved since 1979. Nineteen eighty-four was expected to see fourteen more plants allowed to operate, tying the record for plants brought on-line in the banner year of 1974.

But not even Walske's enthusiasm could conceal the fact that the future facing the nuclear industry was far from rosy. At the end of 1982, U.S. utilities were committed to a total of 147 plants and an aggregate nuclear generating capacity of nearly 136,000 megawatts. But the combination of the 1982 and 1984 plant cancellations had reduced the nuclear commitment to 140 and dropped the industry's aggregate generating capacity to 130,000 megawatts.[6]

And as even Walske conceded, the number of cancellations could well increase. No one, either in the nuclear industry or out of it, who values his money is betting against the cancellation of any of the fifty-six plants that 1984 found in various stages of construction around the U.S. And no one, including Walske himself, denied that growth in the nuclear industry had not only slowed down but ground to a halt. American reactor builders—General Electric Company, Westinghouse, Combustion Engineering, and Babcock and Wilcox—may have had a few orders on their books, but none were from U.S. utilities; all were from abroad.

---

*The figure refers to the amount of power a nuclear plant is capable of delivering when it is operating at capacity at any given moment.

Cautioning members of his industry not to give up and urging them to take heart, Walske warned AIF members that a continuation of the economic recovery that began in 1983 and showed every sign of continuing through the election year of 1984 could confront them with a challenge, and suggested that they hold themselves ready for "the next round of ordering." But utility executives, who are the ones who would do any such ordering, were neither reaching for their checkbooks or anticipating doing so. William Dickhoner, president of the troubled Cincinnati Gas and Electric Company, spoke for many of his fellow utility executives when he observed that "the financial markets have a perception that nuclear units in general are in trouble. We could have put up the money to complete this [Zimmer] unit and had the finest nuclear plant in the country. But we still have no assurance that we would get an operating license."[7]

Another executive was even more blunt. W. S. White, Jr., chairman of the giant American Electric Power Company, viewed the scene and said simply, "No utility executive in his right mind would consider for more than 30 seconds building a nuclear plant today."[8] White was not alone in his view. Robert Scherer, president of Georgia Power and chairman of the strongly pronuclear U.S. Committee for Energy Awareness, looked sadly at the shambles the 1984 cancellations had made of the nuclear power industry and echoed White's lament: "No utility executive in the country would consider ordering a nuclear plant today . . . unless he wanted to be certified or committed."[9]

Some utility executives were even wondering what to do with the nuclear plants they had. Their concern was understandable; the plants are not unlike the sacred white elephants that old Siamese kings presented to fractious subjects, who were not only required to feed the beasts, but since they could not sell them or give them away, to go broke in the process. The rising costs of building and operating nuclear plants had made nuclear electricity, which was touted for its low cost, only slightly less expensive than that produced by coal overall and actually more costly than that produced by coal in certain areas of the U.S.

Nor was this the only problem that companies that owned nuclear power plants, particularly plants still under construction, had to confront as 1984 began. The tremendous cost overruns that have characterized nuclear plant construction had saddled several companies with staggering—and seemingly uncontrollable—debts. New York's Long Island Lighting Company, whose 820-megawatt Shoreham plant was originally expected to come on-line in 1977 at a cost of $350 million, had already spent $1.5 billion and expected the plant to end up costing around $2.2 billion before it went on-line early in 1985. LILCO conceded early in 1984 that it was having a cash-flow problem, due in large part to the fact that it was paying more than $1 million a day to carry the interest on its Shoreham construction loans. It also admitted that it was losing $1.5 million for each day that the plant's start-up was delayed.[10]

Consumers Power Company of Michigan found itself in an equally perilous condition. Having already spent $3.4 billion on its Midland plant, it started the year by revealing that it, too, was spending $1 million a day in interest just to keep the project going and dropping deeper into debt as it did. As of February 1984, Consumers' long-term debt exceeded the company's equity by more than $1 billion, a situation that prompted Consumers' chairman, John D. Selby, to warn that if Midland's reactors were not finished and allowed to operate, the company, which serves 1.3 million electric consumers, could be forced into bankruptcy.[11]

Other companies were in similar straits. Rating agencies lowered their ratings on bonds issued by several electric utilities with large nuclear power plants under construction. In early 1984 Moody's Investors Service dropped its rating on bonds issued by Public Service of Indiana from Baa-2 to Ba-2 after the company announced that it was abandoning its Marble Hill plant. Standard and Poor's warned Illinois's Commonwealth Edison that its BBB+ rating could be reduced as a result of the NRC's decision to deny it a license to operate the Byron plant.[12]

These actions hurt the companies, impairing their efforts to raise capital and to keep their projects going. They also hurt utility company stockholders, who could see the value of their holdings shrink as the problems faced by the companies mounted. The value of LILCO stock, for example, had dropped by 39 percent during 1983, falling from $17 to $10.13 a share and costing the company's 181,227 stockholders something in the neighborhood of $70 million.[13]

The companies' problems also hurt their customers. LILCO expected that its customers might ultimately have to pay up to 50 percent more for their electricity to help defray the costs of getting the Shoreham plant on-line. The Public Service Company of New Hampshire estimated that if its Seabrook 2 plant ever went on-line it would have to raise its rates by as much as 50 percent to recover its investment in the often-delayed plant.[14] Nor did those companies that found themselves forced to abandon plants expect their customers to escape paying at least some of the costs of their mistakes. Public Service of Indiana sought permission from its state's public utility commission to pass some of its losses on its Marble Hill plant along to Hoosier electric consumers.

Consumers in some states took satisfaction from newly enacted laws aimed at preventing utility companies from sticking them for the costs of their errors. But consumers quickly realized that any such victory was likely to prove Pyrrhic. Even those companies not allowed to pass their losses on to their customers directly would still be able to make the public foot at least part of the bill for uncompleted or abandoned nuclear power plants. Federal law allows utilities that write off their construction costs to deduct 30 percent of the amount from their federal tax payments.

To describe consumers as bitter about the situation understated the facts. Consumer groups in New Hampshire, Michigan, Pennsylvania, and other states were lobbying for legislation forcing utility companies and their shareholders to bear the financial burdens of the companies' poor judgment. "Why should we be the victims of the utility companies' greed, bad judgment, and poor management?" asked a Pennsylvanian lobbying for a bill that would make General Public Utilities, the parent of the company that operated the Three Mile Island nuclear power plant, absorb all the costs of cleaning up after the 1979 accident. "Why should power companies be rewarded for bad judgment with guaranteed profits? Why shouldn't power company shareholders take the same risks as the holders of stock in any other publicly held company?"

Utility company executives naturally found themselves embarrassed by such questions, and answered them by noting that if they are forced out of business their failures would affect far more than just their shareholders. But utility company executives were also bitter about the plight in which they—sometimes through their own doing— found themselves. Looking at the wreckage of the industry in the wake of the 1984 plant cancellations, one spokesman found himself unable to see the nuclear industry as anything but a victim. "The first lesson we've learned is this," said Don Beeth, director of nuclear information at Houston Lighting and Power. "Don't build nuclear plants in America. You subject yourself to financial risk and public abuse." Cincinnati Gas and Electric President Dickhoner sounded a similar note when he said, "It's almost a punitive deal to open a nuclear plant anymore."[15]

With no new plants on order and with the future of a good number of those under construction clouded, to say the least, some power company executives saw the prospects for nuclear power as poor or worse. They saw nuclear power plants as the last of the dinosaurs, giants doomed to extinction by changes they had not anticipated and to which they could not adjust. "Some days, I think that I may be building the last nuclear plant that's going to be built for a while," said Georgia Power's Senior Vice President Richard E. Conway early in 1984. "They are just too expensive for a company like us to build any more." His statement was not made casually or in exaggeration. Georgia Power's Plant Vogtle, a two-unit facility just over 50 percent finished in mid-1984, was expected to come in at ten times its original price tag of $635 million.

But most utility company officials felt that the industry would survive. Indeed, most felt that the industry would somehow manage to make it through its present plague of problems and actually recover. Robert Scherer felt that the doldrums in which the industry found itself would persist for a while, particularly given the NRC's newly acquired emphasis on safety. Donald Hodel, then-chief of the federal Department of Energy (he moved to the Department of Interior in January 1985), was slightly more optimistic. He did not envision nuclear power providing the nation with 50 percent of its electricity in either the near or the more distant future, and he actually questioned whether nuclear power could ever fulfill that much of the country's energy appetite. But he did predict that, sometime in the mid-1990s, nuclear power would peak out at the level at which it could account for anywhere from 15 to 25 percent of the nation's energy mix. "I think it will come back," Hodel said. "I think that eventually the U.S. will say that it needs a continuing nuclear component."[16]

Will it? Will nuclear power not merely survive but, like the legendary Phoenix, experience a rebirth? Or will it continue to slide down the slope it has already begun to descend until it reaches the bottom and disappears? And more important, *should* nuclear power survive?

Edward Merrow, the director of energy policy programs at the Rand Corporation, argued early in 1984 that nuclear power's friends and enemies had both missed the point of the plight in which the industry found itself. The question, as he saw it, was not whether the U.S. nuclear power industry was alive or dead, recovering or dying. The question, Merrow said, was whether the U.S. should care. And the answer, at least as far as he was concerned, was yes.

The reason for Merrow's affirmation was practical rather than philosophical. According to Merrow, the question that the U.S. must answer is not whether nuclear power is nice, but whether it is necessary. He, as he made clear, personally believes that it is, particularly considering the alternatives. Merrow conceded that coal, which the U.S. possesses in abundance, may look attractive to people worried about radiation or nuclear accidents. But, like the Old Philosopher noting that there is no such thing as a free lunch, Merrow warned the atom's enemies that coal is not without cost. For generating large amounts of electricity, Merrow said, coal is the only alternative to nuclear power. But coal presents the U.S. with its own set of problems, not the least of which are air pollution and acid rain.[17]

Nor, Merrow maintained, are so-called "alternative" energy sources likely to make a significant contribution to American energy requirements before the end of the century, if they did so at that time. Neither solar nor wind energy technology is sufficiently well developed to generate large amounts of electric power. Nor does nuclear fusion, in which light atoms of hydrogen extracted from seawater are fused rather than split to provide energy, seem likely to provide the answer. Fusion, at least in theory, is cleaner and safer than nuclear fission. But fusion plants are unlikely to sprout around the U.S. for many years, Merrow noted. Scientists working at places like Princeton University in New Jersey or the Lawrence Livermore Laboratory in California have not yet managed to achieve self-sustaining fusion reaction in their laboratories. Until they do, they cannot even begin to turn their attention toward designing commercial fusion reactors.

This, said Merrow, means realistically that for the foreseeable future the U.S. is going to have to rely on either nuclear or coal, or, more likely, nuclear *and* coal, for its energy needs. This means, in turn, that somewhere down the road, the U.S. is going to need nuclear power, not necessarily to provide all its energy, but to provide at least some of it. Said Merrow: "We need the nuclear option."

But can the U.S. nuclear industry meet this need? Can the industry, its confidence in itself shaken, its technological and economic health compromised, and its credibility eroded, somehow manage not merely to remain alive but to recover? Can the nuclear industry extricate itself from the morass in which it is mired?

The answers to these questions depend, in large part, on an understanding of how the nuclear power industry got where it is to begin with. Why is the U.S. nuclear power industry in such moribund condition? What are its past and present problems? What went wrong?

Put these questions to at least some nuclear industry executives and the answers will be that the problems plaguing the industry are external. Many in the industry attribute all its ills to the antinuclear movement, and speak of it as if it were some monolithic force. As they see it, environmentalists, people whom they see as being more interested in birds and flowers than jobs and economic security, are a major part of the problem. It is the environmentalists' use of the courts to delay the construction of nuclear power plants that has stretched the average time from the initial application to the opening of the plant to fourteen years. It is delays like this that have sent the costs of nuclear plant construction skyrocketing, beggaring the companies that attempt to undertake such projects.

As many in the industry see it, the antinuclear movement is the major cause of nuclear power's problems. It is this movement that has, after all, raised questions about nuclear safety, stirred what the industry considers unrealistic fears about radiation, and pandered to what many, both in the industry and outside, call a "Hiroshima syndrome," which leaves otherwise sensible people unable to distinguish between nuclear weapons and nuclear power and eager to ban one to control the other.

Others attribute all of the industry's problems to the accident that occurred in 1979 at Three Mile Island, in which a series of mechanical malfunctions and operator errors brought a nuclear plant to within an hour of starting down the one-way road to a meltdown, and turned a Pennsylvania landmark into a symbol of one of the age's technological nightmares. The accident at Three Mile Island, which sent many residents of southern Pennsylvania fleeing to safety and forced Pennsylvania Governor Richard Thornburgh to consider ordering an evacuation of the area, caught both the industry and the agency charged with regulating it by surprise. It did more than merely reinforce the beliefs of those in the antinuclear movement who had been saying for years that nuclear power plants were dangerous. The accident also cost the industry many of its friends, who were converted from supporters to opponents as quickly and as dramatically as Saint Paul was converted on the road to Damascus.

Nor was this all the Three Mile Island accident cost the industry. The accident led to a lengthy investigation and an NRC list of some six thousand steps that utilities had to take in order to improve the safety of their plants. The accident led to expensive reforms involving operator training, the development of evacuation plans, and the installation of a good deal of extremely expensive hardware, not just on the plants under construction, but on those already in operation as well. In addition, the accident produced a much tougher attitude on the part of the NRC, which had, until then, been somewhat less than assiduous when it came to policing the nuclear power industry. Applying the lessons of Three Mile Island cost the nuclear power industry billions of dollars and significantly slowed its expansion. It led to changes in the licensing process that seem certain to keep any utility from moving quickly or inexpensively to build itself a nuclear plant. "TMI is the worst thing that could have happened to the nuclear power industry," said one utility executive. "If it hadn't been for that accident and the way the press played it up and exaggerated the dangers, I think we'd be in good shape. But the accident killed us . . . or the accident helped the environmentalists kill us." [18]

There is no question that opposition from environmentalists and other elements of the antinuclear movement, which is not monolithic but a loose coalition of groups interested in everything from reducing radiation risks to preserving local rivers and streams for fishermen, has hurt the nuclear power industry, sometimes seriously. Nor is there any question that the accident at Three Mile Island inflicted serious wounds of its own and strengthened the hand of the antinuclear movement significantly.

But is it fair or realistic to blame all of the industry's problems on either the antinuclear movement or the accident and its aftermath, or even on a combination of these things? An honest observer would have to answer no. The industry's ailments are due to a whole congeries of causes. Part of the industry's problem can be traced to the twin "oil shocks" that hit the world during the 1970s, triggering what turned out to be an unnecessary expansion of the industry and raising what turned out to be unreasonable expectations about the industry's future. Part of the industry's problem can be attributed to Americans' totally unexpected response to rising energy prices. Instead of continuing to consume power at their accustomed rates, Americans turned to conservation with a vengeance, so curbing their consumption that utilities suddenly found themselves with more generating capacity than they needed, always a dangerous situation in a world where one of the few laws that always seems to apply is that of supply and demand.

These, however, are only minor parts of the nuclear industry's problem. The major causes of the industry's plight can be found in the industry itself. "Pogo the Possum said it best," said a former AIF official when asked to comment on the state of the industry early in 1984. "He said, 'We have met the enemy and he is us.' "[19]

His statement is more than simple sarcasm. To a greater extent than it has been or still is willing to concede, the nuclear industry has been and remains its own worst enemy. One of its flaws has been arrogance. A few utility companies responded to the changing energy use patterns of the seventies by scaling down their expansion plans and canceling orders for nuclear power plants. But too many others, encouraged by the Reagan administration's strongly pronuclear posture, ignored the omens and pressed on with plans to expand their generating capacity in the unjustified expectation that declining demand would start climbing again. Still others kept on with the construction of nuclear plants out of pride, the old Greek sin of *hubris,* or in the mistaken belief that it was more economical to complete the multibillion-dollar projects than it was to abandon them.

Another of the nuclear industry's flaws, and one that could prove fatal, has been bad judgment. Many companies continued to build nuclear power plants in the assumption that they would be cheaper, both to build and to operate, than coal-fired facilities. That assumption proved erroneous. With post–Three Mile Island requirements pushing the costs of building nuclear power plants steadily upward, coal has steadily become increasingly competitive and nuclear power increasingly uneconomical, a disastrous failing in a world in which profits are paramount.

That mistake would have been bad enough. But the nuclear power industry has been guilty of others. It has committed the sin of poor management of plants under construction. Many nuclear power plants, experts agree, are badly designed. The construction of these facilities, which is generally done by an army of contractors under the general supervision of the utility ordering the plant, has often been poorly supervised. The result of this laxness is work that can often best be described as shoddy. Some of the earthquake supports for California's Diablo Canyon plant were installed backward, as was the reactor vessel at the San Onofre plant near San Diego. Reactor supports at Comanche Peak in Texas were put in 45 degrees out of alignment. Pipes inside and outside the Shoreham reactor were installed so that they failed to meet properly and had to be connected with elbow joints.

Why has the nuclear industry made such mistakes? A main reason, according to experts, is that it has grown too quickly, expanding from a fledgling outgrowth of the Manhattan Project to a major U.S.

industry in a little over two decades, and rushing to build larger and
larger plants before it had fully mastered the technology involved in
building and operating smaller ones. "We should have been a little
slower in moving; the enormous rush of orders really stressed the
system," admitted Robert Scherer. Victor Gilinsky, a former member of the Nuclear Regulatory Commission and a frequent critic of
the industry, took a similar tack. "We got ahead of ourselves in expanding and scaling up the applications of nuclear power as fast as
we did," he said.[20]

In retrospect, it is easy to see that they are correct. Looking
backward, it is clear that the excitement over atomic energy and its
potential as a power source simply caused some bright people to leave
their prudence and common sense behind and to jump aboard a jug-
gernaut before being aware of the problems or the complexities involved with what they were doing. Many utility men refused to see
nuclear power as anything more than a new way to boil water, ignoring the fact that they were dealing with a complicated and, even
today, experimental technology.

The U.S. government, which encouraged the development of the
nuclear power industry, must share in the blame for its present plight.
From the start, the government showed more interest in promoting
the growth of nuclear power than in regulating it. For years, the
government, through the Atomic Energy Commission, sheltered the
fledgling nuclear power industry from the realities of the marketplace, underwriting a large part of the price of reactor development,
helping to assure it a cheap supply of fuel, ignoring growing public
concerns over nuclear safety and worries about how nuclear power
plants were being built and operated. In the end, this policy did the
industry more harm than good, for when the necessity for choosing
between the role of promoter and regulator forced the government
to opt for regulation and to push the nuclear power industry out of
the nest the AEC had feathered, the industry proved unable to fly
on its own. Like a bird that had not quite developed or like a plane
that should never have gotten off the drawing board, much less the
ground, it soared briefly, then began to fall.

It has fallen far. But it has not yet crashed. The question now is,
can it pull up in time? The answer to this question cannot come from
the federal government, which can streamline its regulations and
procedures to eliminate undue delays in the licensing process without compromising safety. Nor can the answer come from the scientific community, which can determine the risks involved in obtain-

ing a substantial fraction of America's electric energy from nuclear power, but which cannot usurp the public's prerogative of deciding whether the benefits of doing so justify accepting those risks. The answer cannot come from the U.S. public, which cannot be expected to endorse nuclear power for emotional or political reasons, but which can only be expected to support it if its members agree that it meets the country's needs and is capable of providing the U.S. with energy that it cannot get—or get more cheaply—from other sources. The answer must come from the industry itself.

But, then, what must the industry do in order to find and provide this answer? That would seem to be obvious. The industry must carefully review its own history and evaluate its performance over the past three decades. It must recognize where it went wrong and made mistakes, and just as important, recognize and build upon what it did right. Like the hunter lost in the forest, it must not panic, and as an old saying goes, "run in circles, scream, and shout." It must pause, sit down, and take careful stock of its situation. It must figure out where it is and how it got there and, instead of blindly crashing off through the brush in search of salvation, take some time to figure out where it wants to go and how to get there.

The condition of the U.S. nuclear power industry is critical but not irreversible. Its situation is also ironic. The nuclear age began with such promise. . . .

Two

In the Beginning . . .

It all started with such promise. The age of commercial nuclear power can be said, if an official birth date is needed, to have begun on Labor Day, 1954. It began when President Dwight Eisenhower, popular and trusted, appeared on national television from Denver, Colorado. Eisenhower was not one of the nation's greatest speakers; his tortured syntax drove grammarians to distraction and journalists to bursts of parody. But the former general had a keen sense of public relations and knew the value of a good gesture. In his broadcast, he made just such a gesture. Waving a "magic wand," he signaled an unmanned, radio-controlled bulldozer to begin breaking ground two thousand miles away at the small Pennsylvania town of Shippingport, ninety miles north of Pittsburgh on the Ohio River.[1] The purpose of the groundbreaking: to begin construction of the nation's—and the world's—first commercial nuclear power plant, a joint venture involving the Duquesne Light and Power Company of Pittsburgh and the recently formed Atomic Energy Commission.

The plant was to be the showpiece of the U.S.'s much-heralded "Atoms for Peace" program. The program was a massive—and well-intentioned—effort to help the atom to live down its lethal reputation. Nuclear power had, after all, made its first public appearance as an instrument of war.

In fact, many Americans were unaware that the atom could be

used for anything but destruction. Atomic devices had been exploded in the deserts of the American Southwest, convincing scientists that the power contained in the atom could be used to level cities. Atomic bombs had been exploded over the Japanese cities of Hiroshima and Nagasaki, accomplishing in seconds the kind of devastation that could otherwise have been accomplished only by exploding thousands of tons of more conventional bombs. The two atomic bombs hastened the end of the war and spared the U.S. from conducting a land invasion of Japan. They also blasted into the minds of many scientists, as well as many ordinary people, a fear of the atom and its awesome power, a fear that remains unabated.

Which is unfortunate. The atom itself is an innocent thing, devoid of politics, philosophy, or intent.

The idea of the atom, in fact, goes back more than two thousand years. It was a Greek who first conceived the idea. Democritus of Thrace (470 to 380 B.C.) had traveled widely in Egypt and the Near East, observed carefully, and developed some surprisingly modern ideas. He maintained, for example, that the Milky Way was a vast conglomeration of tiny stars. He also theorized that all matter was composed of tiny particles so infinitesimally small that nothing smaller was even conceivable. These particles were thus *atomos*, or indivisible. They were, as far as Democritus was concerned, also eternal, immutable, and indestructible. Besides themselves and the void, or the space between them, Democritus maintained, nothing else existed. Even the human mind and the gods (if they existed, and Democritus was not sure that they did) were composed of atoms.

These atoms were not all the same, Democritus reasoned. They differed from each other physically, and their differences explained the properties of various substances. Thus, he explained, the atoms of water were smooth and round, which was why water flowed and had no permanent shape. The atoms of fire were more like thorns, which explained why burns were so painful. The atoms of earth were rough and jagged, which was why they held together and formed a hard surface.[2]

Scientists down through the ages did not question Democritus— if they thought of him at all. The great seventeenth-century English physicist Isaac Newton certainly did not. "It seems probable to me," he wrote, "that God in the Beginning formed Matter in solid, massy, hard, impenetrable, moveable particles . . . so very hard as never to wear or break in pieces, no ordinary Power being able to divide what God Himself made one in the first Creation."[3]

Newton may have been certain. He was also wrong. So were the modern scientists who dismissed the notion of atomic fission, which both Albert Einstein and Sir Ernest Rutherford had theorized in the 1920s. Their error was ironic. In the early 1930s, the Italian-born physicist Enrico Fermi actually succeeded in splitting atoms in his University of Chicago laboratory, without realizing what he had done. The reason that he did not was philosophical. On the basis of his theoretical calculations, Fermi had concluded that fission was not possible.

But Fermi was hardly the only scientist to underestimate the possibilities inherent in the atom. In 1933 Rutherford, one of the greatest contributors to the understanding of atomic structures, spoke before the British Association for the Advancement of Science, where he declared: "The energy produced by the breaking down of the atom is a very poor kind of thing. Anyone who expects a source of power from the transformation of these atoms is talking moonshine."[4]

What convinced Fermi that he was wrong and started others on the search for ways to split atoms was the discovery, late in 1938, that nuclear fission was indeed possible. In experiments conducted at the Kaiser Wilhelm Institute in Berlin, chemists Otto Hahn and Fritz Strassmann found that the center of the uranium atom, its nucleus, could be split apart, that it could, quite literally, be broken in two.

The theoretical implications of this discovery, which were quickly formulated by physicists Lise Meitner and Otto Frisch, were staggering. Shortly after Hahn and Strassmann made their discovery, the Danish physicist Niels Bohr arrived in the U.S. with the news. Ten days later, at the end of January 1939, Bohr and Fermi discussed the phenomenon at the Fifth Washington Conference on Theoretical Physics. Within days word of the discovery had made its way to laboratories around the U.S., giving a new urgency to experiments in physics and chemistry and opening up broad new avenues of speculation. Scientists in nearly a dozen countries published papers relating to atomic fission. Fermi and the Hungarian-born Leo Szilard, working at Columbia University in New York, measured the release and absorption of neutrons in uranium and made a preliminary report of their results in July 1939. In September Bohr and John A. Wheeler of Princeton University published what has since been recognized as the classical analysis of the fission phenomenon.[5]

The excitement generated by the discovery of fission was such that scientists would have worked intensely whatever the geopoliti-

cal climate. Most scientists already understood that fuller understanding of nuclear reactions could lead to the development of weapons of unprecedented power. Anyone who doubted that this was so
needed only to listen to the talk around the laboratories or listen to
the reports coming in from overseas, especially from Germany, where
new discoveries made many scientists realize that Hitler's Reich had
the technology to exploit this discovery. Indeed, intelligence reports, as inconclusive as they were alarming, indicated that efforts
were already under way in German laboratories to do just this.

This information had its greatest impact upon those U.S.-based
scientists who had fled from countries threatened or controlled by
the Nazis, which is why, on March 16, 1939, and at the encourage-
ment of Szilard and Eugene Wigner of Princeton, Fermi briefed U.S.
military officials on the Columbia experiments and told them that a
chain reaction in uranium might have major military applications.[6]
It is also why, in August of that same year, Einstein wrote to President Franklin Roosevelt to tell him that "the new phenomenon would
also lead to the construction of bombs, and it is conceivable—though
much less certain—that extremely powerful bombs of a new type may
thus be constructed." Prophetically, Einstein went on: "A single bomb
of this type, carried by boat and exploded in a port, might very well
destroy the port together with some of the surrounding territory."
Einstein urged coordination between the government and the scientific community and noted darkly that Germany had stopped the
sale of uranium from mines in Czechoslovakia, which it had recently
taken over, suggesting that Germany was at work on a bomb.[7]

The Einstein letter proved effective. Presented to the President
by economist Alexander Sachs, it persuaded Roosevelt to authorize
the National Academy of Sciences to appoint an advisory committee
on uranium and to coordinate fission research.[8]

The committee agreed with Einstein. On November 1, 1939, it
reported that a chain reaction in uranium was possible, and suggested what this might mean to the nation. "If [a chain reaction] could
be achieved and controlled," said the report, "it might supply power
for submarines. If the reaction should be explosive, it would provide
a possible source of bombs with a destructiveness vastly greater than
anything now known."[9]

The appointment of a committee did not, however, provide a
meaningful impetus to research. Chaired by Lyman J. Briggs, director of the National Bureau of Standards, the committee was as conservative as the scientists with whom it dealt. Most of the latter still

thought of fission as a scientific rather than a military project. So it was not until the spring of 1940 that fission research really began to pick up momentum. The man who helped provide it was Vannevar Bush, director of Washington's Carnegie Institute and head of the newly formed National Defense Research Committee. Bush reorganized the advisory committee on uranium and got research started in several areas. He also started a discussion of where scientists should direct their efforts—building bombs, developing power plants for submarines, or separating the isotope U-235, the most fissionable form of the substance, from natural uranium.[10]

Bush was only one of those responsible for the birth of the atomic age. Another major contributor was Glenn T. Seaborg, who had won his Ph.D. from the University of California at Berkeley in 1937 and stayed on to conduct research. Seaborg had been enormously excited by the news of the Hahn-Strassmann experiment, and, determined to win himself some fame as a scientist, he worked closely with another Berkeley researcher, Edwin McMillan, in attempts to synthesize a new element. He soon succeeded. Shortly after McMillan left Berkeley to do research on the development of radar at the Massachusetts Institute of Technology, Seaborg and his colleagues came up with proof that they had made an element that was chemically different from all known elements. They named their new discovery plutonium, after the planet Pluto, and they soon discovered that it possessed an unusual property. Plutonium, they found, could be fissioned; what is more, it could be fissioned more easily than U-235.

The implications of this discovery were enormous. U-235 is very rare, accounting for less than one percent of natural uranium. Plutonium, made from the much more abundant U-238, could be produced in almost limitless quantities, providing a virtually unlimited supply of either fuel or explosive material.[11]

The implications of another discovery were even more startling. Working under a new agency called the Office of Scientific Research and Development, scientists like Fermi, Szilard, and others had moved from Columbia to the University of Chicago. There, under the stands of the University's Stagg Field, they began a project that would, quite literally, change the world—the construction of the world's first nuclear reactor.

Constructed in an unused squash court, the University of Chicago reactor was called an "atomic pile," because that, in fact, is what it was. Intended to produce the world's first chain reaction—in which the neutron escaping from the fissioning of one uranium atom would strike the nucleus of the next atom and cause that to split as well, triggering a process that would result in the rapid-fire fissioning of atoms and the release of unprecedented amounts of energy—the reactor consisted of a pile of graphite blocks in which uranium was embedded. To limit and control the reaction, the scientists inserted control rods of a material that would absorb neutrons. These control rods would thus regulate the rate at which fissioning took place. As a special safety precaution, to be used in case the reaction got out of control, a special, superabsorbent rod was suspended by a rope over a slot in the pile. Next to the rope holding the rod was an axe. It was there so that if the reaction got to be too much to handle, a safety officer could pick it up and cut the rope, dropping the control rod into the reactor and, it was hoped, shutting it off. The man assigned to perform this task was called the "safety control rod ax man." His title persists in the nuclear power industry to this day. The emergency shutdown of a nuclear reactor, now accomplished by complex, automated equipment, is still referred to by the acronym SCRAM.[12]

Fermi, now convinced, of course, that fission was indeed possible, had calculated how his carefully designed reactor should work in theory. He had no idea how it would work in practice. But he soon learned. Just before 3:30 on the afternoon of December 3, 1941, as Fermi and others watched, physicist George Weil withdrew the main control rod from the pile, and, exactly as the scientists had predicted it would, a chain reaction began. The reaction was not allowed to go on for very long; Fermi ordered the control rods replaced and the reactor shut off after it had run for a mere twenty-eight minutes and produced a few watts of heat. The reactor had run long enough; it showed that a chain reaction was possible and that the energy inside the uranium atom could be extracted and put to use. It also provided the basis of nuclear reactor design. Though modern nuclear reactors are more sophisticated than the University of Chicago "pile," they are built on the same principle. In all nuclear reactors, fissionable fuel is brought together in amounts sufficient to create a critical mass, in which the neutrons released in the normal process of atomic decay can find a sufficient number of similar atoms with which they can interact in a chain reaction. Control rods of neutron-absorbing graphite or boron control the reactions. When the rods are fully withdrawn, the reactor can operate at 100 percent of its capacity; when they are pulled only halfway out, the reactor operates at 50 percent power. When they are inserted all the way, the reactor shuts down.

The success of the Chicago reactor and the diffuse nature of nuclear research in the U.S. convinced Bush that something had to be done to coordinate the work then going on at such places as Oak Ridge, Tennessee, Hanford, Washington, and Los Alamos, New Mexico. He was certain that no civilian agency could find the resources, either financial or administrative, to construct and operate these installations. So he successfully urged the U.S. Army to do something. In August 1942, it set up a program under the cover name of the Manhattan Engineering District, which quickly become known as the Manhattan Project, and shortly thereafter named general Leslie R. Groves to head it.[13]

Groves moved quickly. Within days of his appointment, he had visited the three installations and begun to assemble the team of scientists who would give the U.S.—and the world—the first atomic bomb.

The feverish wartime efforts to produce an atomic bomb culminated in the world's first nuclear explosion at the so-called Trinity site near Alamogordo, New Mexico, on July 16, 1945.[14] But the wartime research had effectively precluded any study of the atom's more peaceful applications. Scientists had been working for more than a year on two types of bombs, one using uranium, the other plutonium, for their explosive force. Those scientists who had reservations about what they were doing—and many, feeling that the role of science was to make life better rather than end it, did—were persuaded that the development of a nuclear bomb would shorten the war and bring untold benefits to the world in the peace that would follow the conflict.

There is no question that the bombs that resulted from their work did the former. The uranium bomb that was dropped on Hiroshima on August 6, 1945, and the plutonium bomb that was dropped on the tactically unimportant city of Nagasaki three days later destroyed both cities (although the Nagasaki bomb landed slightly off target) and caused a total of 300,000 deaths, some of them instant, others delayed by as many as five years.[15]

The two bombs also forced the Japanese government, which the U.S. and its allies did not realize had virtually exhausted its war-making capacity, to sue for peace and to accept the U.S. demand that it surrender unconditionally. Within two months, the war in the Pacific was over.

And a new era was beginning. Many of those who had worked on the atomic bomb were appalled at what their research had created and sought only to find a way by which the nuclear genie could somehow be recaptured and reimprisoned in the bottle from which they had released him. But others, more realistic and perhaps more ambitious as well, realized that now that the genie had been released he was free for good. But not necessarily beyond their control. The force of the atom, they believed, could—and should—be harnessed to power ships, planes, and electric generating plants, to heat and cool cities, to run industries, and to make life better for mankind.

Few of these "true believers," maybe none of them, were more evangelistic than Glenn Seaborg. As a Manhattan Project scientist, Seaborg had signed a secret report to the Secretary of War urging that the power of the atomic bomb be demonstrated to the Japanese by dropping it on a barren island rather than on an inhabited city. As Seaborg saw it, civilization's future was in the hands of the nuclear scientists, who comprised an elite group that could "build a new world through nuclear technology." He envisioned a world of atom-powered abundance, saw nuclear energy as a magic power that could free mankind from its limitations. Without much prompting, Seaborg would wax eloquent about the new science, predicting a future in which millions of homes would be heated and lit by the power of a single nuclear reactor, in which ships and planes could sail or fly almost forever on the energy contained in a pocket-sized piece of plutonium, in which the whole planet could be virtually made over, mountain ranges leveled, deserts made to bloom, rivers controlled, by the forces that he and his colleagues had helped to put at man's disposal. "Where science fiction goes," asked Seaborg, "can the atom be far behind?" [16]

Seaborg was nothing if not sure of the answer to his rhetorical question. His only fear, he confessed, was that he might be "underestimating the possibilities."

The possibilities at that point, though, were still largely on paper. Because of the war effort, few of the scientists involved in nuclear research had given much thought to the problems of designing nuclear power reactors or of turning their other dreams of cheap, abundant energy into reality. Many of those who might have done so were also uncertain as to whether—or how—nuclear power should be controlled. Toward the end of the war, a Manhattan Project task force had been asked to develop a policy on postwar nuclear research. Headed by R. C. Tolman, dean of the California Institute of Technology, the committee was not enthusiastic about the commercial applications of the atom. Indeed, its report concluded: "The development of fission piles solely for the production of power for ordinary commercial use does not appear economically sound nor advisable from the point of view of preserving national resources." Or, to put it more bluntly, the committee felt that fissionable uranium was too valuable to use for generating electric power.[17]

This view, however, proved to be a minority opinion, even within the scientific community. The majority of scientists shared Seaborg's vision. Robert M. Hutchins, chancellor of the University of Chicago, which had hosted much Manhattan Project research, looked forward to a time when "a very few individuals working a few hours a day at very easy tasks in the central atomic power plant will provide all the heat, light and power required by a community and these utilities will be so cheap that their cost can hardly be reckoned." Physicist and writer George Gamow published a book in 1946 titled *Atomic Energy in Cosmic and Human Life*. In it, he said that "the newly discovered possibility of liberating the hidden energy of uranium atoms promises us an almost unbelievable technical progress in the years to come." David E. Lilienthal, head of the Tennessee Valley Authority and later President Harry S. Truman's nominee to head the newly formed Atomic Energy Commission, hailed the "almost limitless beneficial applications of atomic energy."[18]

There were, of course, some doubters singing counterpoint to these paeans of praise for the atom. A handful of economists wondered if nuclear power would ever really be competitive with other more conventional energy sources. But the public was sold on the new technology and listened avidly to scientific and science fiction forecasts of the coming atomic utopia, about which science editor David Dietz wrote late in 1945 for the Scripps-Howard newspapers: "No baseball game will be called off on account of rain in the Era of Atomic Energy. No airplane will by-pass an airport because of fog. No city will experience a winter traffic jam because of heavy snow. Summer resorts will be able to guarantee the weather and artificial suns will make it as easy to grow corn and potatoes indoors as on the farm."[19]

But even had scientists, economists, and the public been completely united in their enthusiasm, the path to the nuclear millennium of which they dreamed was anything but straight. Congress and the Truman administration may, as did the President himself, have wanted to make a blessing of nuclear power. But a number of obstacles stood in the way of this goal, among them the Cold War between the U.S. and its former ally, the U.S.S.R. Scientists tended to sound as if they were writing science fiction when they testified on the commercial applications of nuclear power. But military men tended to sound as if they knew exactly what they were talking about when they discussed the military applications of the atom. So it is hardly surprising that Congress, in passing the Atomic Energy Act of 1946, should have addressed itself far more attentively to the latter than it did to the former. The Atomic Energy Act was designed for the primary purpose of protecting atomic secrets so as to preserve the U.S. monopoly on nuclear weapons and technology. It was also intended to establish an Atomic Energy Commission to provide civilian control over nuclear weaponry. Peaceful uses of atomic energy? The 1946 act mentioned them only in passing.[20]

The Atomic Energy Commission, which officially came into existence in August 1946, was almost instantly overwhelmed by its responsibilities. For one thing, it found itself with more people and facilities than it knew how to handle. It had inherited from the Manhattan Project a huge network of laboratories and manufacturing plants, not to mention more than 40,000 people. Deliberately scattered across the country, these facilities had no central management. Nor did they have a great deal of uranium. The mine in the Belgian Congo that had provided the uranium for the U.S. bomb program was nearly exhausted. The reactors used during the war for making plutonium were wearing out. The U.S. might have thought that it had a stockpile of atomic bombs ready for use. But as David Lilienthal, the AEC's first chairman, reported to a rather stunned President Truman in the spring of 1947, the cupboard was bare. The U.S. had no nuclear weapons manufactured and ready for use. And it had very little uranium with which to make them.[21]

This discovery put the peacetime development of atomic energy on a back burner. The 1949 explosion by the Soviet Union of its own atomic bomb helped keep it there. The AEC had no time to think about developing nuclear power plants; it was concerned with more pressing priorities, the most important of which was keeping the U.S. ahead in an arms race in which, prior to the development of the Soviet bomb, it had been the only contestant.

But even before the Soviet bomb, the AEC had not been ready

to proceed at top speed with the development of atomic power reactors. A 1947 report by J. Robert Oppenheimer, the leading physicist of the Manhattan Project and head of the AEC's General Advisory Committee, damped some of the commission's enthusiasm for
nuclear power plants by arguing that a more realistic evaluation of
their prospects was necessary to balance popular misconceptions about
them. Oppenheimer said that it did not appear hopeful "to use natural uranium directly as an adequate source of fuel for atomic power,"
and predicted that the development of plutonium reactors capable
of producing enough fuel for the utility industry would take decades.
Even Seaborg, ever the enthusiast where nuclear power was concerned, had to concede that Oppenheimer was right. As a member
of the AEC's full advisory committee, he concurred in a report in
which the body said that it did not see how it would be possible "under the most favorable circumstances to have any considerable portion of the present power supply of the world replaced by nuclear
fuel before the expiration of twenty years." [22]

The fact that everyone—from Lilienthal and Seaborg to the people around the President—had to face was that scientific enthusiasm
for nuclear power plants had waned. Most of the scientists involved
with nuclear research were interested in studying the properties of
atoms, not in the nuts and bolts of power plant design, which they
considered "plumbing," and which they knew was not likely to win
any of them Nobel prizes.

Seaborg had gone back to Berkeley after the war to work on dis-
covering more new elements. Other scientists followed suit. The AEC,
however, was reluctant to write off nuclear power. Leaders like Lilienthal feared that pulling the rug out from under public expectations might play into the hands of those who thought of the atom as
exclusively military property and end civilian control of the AEC.
Lewis L. Strauss, who succeeded Lilienthal as commissioner, felt that
admitting that nuclear power was a pipe dream would handicap the
agency in the annual race for appropriations. [23]

Understandably, the agency tried to have it both ways. It down-
played nuclear energy, but insisted that work on the atom's military
applications would ultimately lead to civilian applications, too. Its ploy
was disingenuous. Bombs and reactors worked on vastly different
principles. Weapons research might lead to a better understanding
of the atom, which might prove valuable when researchers turned
their attention to building power reactors. But in no way could

weapons research be considered identical or, in Lilienthal's own words, "the other side of the coin" to developing power reactors.

Work on the peacetime applications of nuclear power was pushed farther into the background by work on the hydrogen bomb. The idea for such a bomb had first been conceived back in 1942 when Fermi asked Edward Teller if the force of an exploding atomic bomb might not be used to start "something similar to the reactions in the sun." What Fermi had in mind were reactions involving deuterons, the nuclei of a rare but naturally occurring form of hydrogen. As Fermi speculated, and as science has since established, under the right combinations of density and temperature, deuterons fuse with each other, producing helium and releasing tremendous amounts of energy. This is essentially what happens within the sun. But back in 1942 Teller doubted that it could be made to happen anywhere else. After some calculation, Teller concluded that deuterium could not be "ignited" by atomic bombs.

Like Fermi's original conclusion on the possibility of fission, Teller's conclusion on fusion was also wrong. Later calculations convinced him that it could indeed be done. Moreover, Teller and others became convinced that it *should* be done. The explosion of the first Soviet atomic bomb, which ended the American nuclear monopoly, fueled their fervor for a "superbomb." The President and the Joint Chiefs of Staff supported their plans to proceed with its development. The outbreak of the Korean conflict in 1950 provided further impetus. Working at full speed, the AEC and its scientists proceeded with work on a thermonuclear device, exploding the first— the so-called "George Shot"—on the Pacific island of Enewetok on May 8, 1951. Over the next three years, they followed this initial experiment with bigger and bigger devices. Finally, on March 1, 1954, they exploded a device with a yield of fifteen megatons—the equivalent of 15 million tons of TNT, or about 15,000 times the power of the bomb that devastated Hiroshima.[24]

The demonstration of what a hydrogen bomb could do horrified many Americans and frightened many of the U.S.'s allies. Many people quickly forgot the postwar dream of the atom as the provider of cheap, abundant power. Instead, they saw it only as an agent of destruction. The prospect of the two postwar superpowers facing each other with hydrogen bombs (the Soviets exploded their own hydrogen bomb a year after the U.S.) impressed large numbers of Americans with the need to rehabilitate the atom and assure that its power would somehow be put to peaceful uses, not used to destroy cities in a war that even then people realized no one would win.

The assurance was provided by President Dwight Eisenhower and his Atoms for Peace program. Speaking before the United Nations General Assembly on December 8, 1953, the President acknowledged that atomic energy could be used to level cities and kill untold thousands. But in a swords-into-plowshares approach borrowed from the Bible, he pledged to use the atom's tremendous power for man's benefit rather than his destruction. "The United States knows that peaceful power from atomic energy is no dream of the future," said the President. "That capability, already proved, is here—now, today." Nuclear power, Eisenhower continued, could "provide abundant electrical energy in the power-starved areas of the world."[25]

Nuclear power, Eisenhower conceded, could be misused. But, he insisted, this abuse could also be prevented. He said: "The U.S. pledges . . . to help solve the fearful atomic dilemma—to devote its entire heart and mind to find the way by which the miraculous inventiveness of man shall not be dedicated to his death, but consecrated to his life."

Eisenhower's appeal proved effective. Reacting to the President's call, the Congressional Joint Committee on Atomic Energy drafted several new laws designed to promote the peaceful use of nuclear power. The most important of these was an amended version of the Atomic Energy Act of 1946. The original act had forbidden the private ownership of nuclear materials. The 1954 act called upon the AEC to license private companies to build and operate nuclear power stations. As an afterthought, the law also charged the AEC with the responsibility for protecting the health and safety of the public.[26]

Under the new law, private companies would be encouraged to build and operate nuclear reactors. The government would retain ownership of all nuclear fuel, but permit its use in privately owned power stations. The law also authorized the government to enter into bilateral agreements with other countries for the peaceful development of atomic power stations, and liberalized patent and secrecy provisions. The law specifically forbade the AEC itself from getting into the electricity supply business. What the law did not do, though, was take the AEC out of the weapons business. The AEC might help promote the use of atoms for peace, but under the terms of the 1954 law, it continued to develop them for war as well.

The AEC took its mandate seriously and launched what Daniel Ford of the Union of Concerned Scientists has described in his 1982 book *The Cult of the Atom* as "the most ambitious construction program in the U.S. since the building of the railroads in the 19th century." Ford's description is accurate. The AEC hoped to have one thousand nuclear power plants in operation around the country by the year 2000.

The AEC did manage to get the first of those plants on-line far sooner than anyone could have expected. It did so because it was, in a sense, able to ride into the nuclear age on a U.S. Navy submarine.

The U.S. Navy had been interested in atomic energy almost from the beginning. Ross Gunn, the technical adviser to the director of the Naval Research Laboratory, realized the potential of nuclear power back in 1939, when Bohr and Fermi first addressed the Fifth Washington Conference on Theoretical Physics. Two months after that meeting, Fermi met with the Navy Department to talk about atomic physics. Most of the naval staff assembled to hear him thought of atomic power in terms of weapons. But Gunn was already thinking about a nuclear-powered engine that could drive a submarine. His interest was understandable. Because a nuclear engine would need no oxygen in order to operate, a submarine powered by one would be freed from the need to surface to recharge its batteries. The only time that such a submarine would have to surface would be to take on provisions.

Excited by the prospect, Gunn contacted Merle Tuve of the Carnegie Institute and, with $1,500 in Navy funds, set up a program to study the idea of nuclear-powered submarines. Tuve's reaction was positive. In 1940 he reported that development of a submarine engine appeared to be more feasible than the construction of an atomic bomb.

The government's decision to concentrate its efforts on the development of a bomb meant that the Navy had to wait before putting its efforts into atomic submarines. But it did not mean that the Navy lost interest in the idea. It continued to follow the development of atomic piles, which is what all early reactors were called.[27]

Atomic piles, meanwhile, were changing. The simple stack of uranium-peppered graphite blocks that Fermi and his colleagues had employed at the University of Chicago to achieve the first chain reaction was being replaced by more complex and more sophisticated devices. In fact, by 1944, a full year before the war ended, researchers had come up with at least five major reactor concepts. Farrington Daniels, a University of Wisconsin chemist working at the Manhattan Project's metallurgy laboratory in Chicago, for example, had come up with the idea for a high-temperature power pile cooled by helium gas. Walter Zinn of the same laboratory had an idea for a reactor that might have been the envy of medieval alchemists; it would produce more fissionable fuel than it consumed. Zinn's idea, which became the basis of the breeder reactor, was to surround the chain-reacting core of a reactor with a "blanket" made of either natural uranium or thorium. Neither U-238, which constitutes at least 99 percent of natural uranium, nor thorium-232 is fissionable. But both have the potential for being so, as the nuclei of both U-238 and thorium-232 will absorb neutrons. When they do, they change. Thorium-232 is transmuted into uranium-233, which is fissionable. U-238 is transmuted to plutonium-239, which Seaborg had shown years earlier to be fissionable. Thus, figured Zinn, a reactor surrounded by these materials would, over a period of time, "breed" more fissionable material than it started with. To utilize this idea, Zinn hoped to build a fast-neutron breeder that would be cooled by liquid metal and that would produce plutonium from enriched U-235.

Others also had ideas about building nuclear reactors. Philip Morrison of the Los Alamos Laboratory proposed to build a 10-kilowatt fast-neutron pile that would use plutonium as its fuel. His idea was unusual. A fast-neutron pile does not use a moderator—material placed in the reactor core to cushion and absorb some of the reaction's very high energy neutrons at the moment of their release from fissioned nuclei. Such a pile is more likely than other types to have a sustained chain reaction, but it is also harder to shut off.

Researchers at Tennessee's Clinton Laboratories, which later became the Oak Ridge National Laboratory, had a radically different idea for a nuclear pile. They conceived of a device in which the fuel would be in a homogeneous state, like a solution of uranium salts in water, rather than in the form of rods or cartridges as in most other reactors. In heterogeneous-fuel reactors, water is circulated around the fuel elements to pick up the heat of the atomic reaction and carry it to a heat exchanger, where it is used to produce steam. In homogeneous-fuel piles, the fuel itself circulates. Once it has become hot from the reactions taking place in it, it is pumped out of the reactor to a heat exchanger, then back into the reactor to be reheated.

The Naval Research Laboratory had an idea of its own. It proposed a reactor that would use sodium-potassium alloy—a metal that liquefies at room temperature—as its coolant. Philip Abelson, then a civilian physicist with the Navy (he is presently editor of the

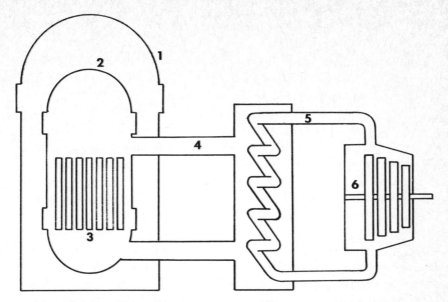

Atomic Energy Made Easy. Though its machinery is complex, the idea of a nuclear power plant is simple. A reinforced concrete containment building (1) houses the reactor (2), which contains a core (3) composed of bundles of pencil-thin rods of uranium fuel. The nuclear reaction within the core heats water, which circulates through the plant's radioactive primary loop (4) and transfers its heat to the non-radioactive secondary loop (5). Steam produced from the heated water in the secondary loop drives a turbine (6), which is harnessed to a generator that produces electricity.
(Diagram by Michael Stoler)

American Association for the Advancement of Science's weekly journal, *Science*) liked the idea of a sodium-cooled reactor. In a 1946 report he urged the Navy to use it and to build a nuclear-powered submarine in two years.[28]

Serious work on nuclear reactor development began with the Daniels reactor, which was set up by the Manhattan Project at Oak Ridge. The Navy became involved when Charles Thomas of Monsanto Chemical Company, whose firm operated the Oak Ridge facility, suggested that the Navy participate in a joint project with industry to build the Daniels reactor. It became more deeply involved in 1946 when General Groves, still the nation's top man where things nuclear were concerned, asked the Navy to send some engineering officers to Oak Ridge to become familiar with nuclear technology and to do the preliminary work on development of a possible nuclear engine. The Navy complied and sent a small group of officers to Tennessee. Its decision proved seminal. The senior officer in the group was a forceful, determined electrical engineer with the rank of captain. His name was Hyman Rickover.[29]

Rickover had not been named as officer in charge of the group, because the leaders of the Navy's Bureau of Ships could not agree on his appointment. It made no difference. Rickover took charge of the group anyway. Under his leadership—and prodding—the group worked without stint to learn nuclear physics and to figure out how this scientific knowledge could be put to the practical use of designing a nuclear engine. The Navy men soon learned that scientists at Oak Ridge were less than impressed by Daniels's idea. But they soon heard a better one. In 1946 Alvin M. Weinberg, the laboratory's top physicist, suggested the idea of using water under high pressure to both moderate the reaction of a core and to carry the heat away to a heat exchanger. The idea appealed to the Navy. Liquid coolant would be far less bulky than gas, enabling the construction of a reactor small enough to fit into the cramped space available on a submarine.[30]

Competition among rival designs eliminated the Daniels reactor from consideration. But Rickover found the idea of a pressurized water reactor appealing, and back in Washington he brought all his technical expertise and bureaucratic skill into play to push for the project.

The Navy had planned to build four reactors. It wanted to develop and construct a land-based prototype and a marine version of the pressurized water. It also wanted to build two versions of the liquid metal–cooled design. It launched its first submarine reactor project in 1948 at the Argonne National Laboratory in Illinois. For the project, the Navy chose the pressurized water reactor. The idea behind the project was to use the reactor to produce heat, which would be used to make steam. The steam, in turn, would be used to turn a turbine that would turn the propeller shaft of a submarine.

Rickover had no doubt that such a system would work. His problem was overcoming the inertia of the agencies involved. To do so, he realized, he would have to keep the project under his personal control and avoid giving any more power than was absolutely necessary to either the bureaucrats or the scientists, the latter being, in his mind, too afraid to move, the former too quick to get sidetracked.

Seaborg, then an AEC adviser, endorsed Rickover's plan, which was to bypass the AEC's scientists and to bring in industrial engineers who would work under his own direction. Rickover took advantage of Seaborg's support to set up an unusual working relationship with Westinghouse Electric Corporation, which built engines and power plants for nonnuclear craft and which was eager to get into the nuclear business. Under Rickover's persuasion, Westinghouse set up a laboratory at the old, little-used Bettis Airport, a small facility thirteen miles south of Pittsburgh. The relationship—not to mention the contract—between Westinghouse and the AEC was . . . well, unique. Most contracts include detailed lists of obligations, specifying what each party to the agreement must do. The Westinghouse contract, drawn up by a young AEC attorney named James T. Ramey, contained no such terms. Under this agreement, the company and the commission promised to work together in "a spirit of partnership and friendly cooperation." Westinghouse would provide the technical expertise for the venture; the AEC would foot the bills for the Bettis operation.[31]

The arrangement raised more than just a few eyebrows. After studying the agreement between the AEC and Westinghouse, Senator Abraham Ribicoff, a Connecticut Democrat, observed that he found it difficult "to determine in the organization scheme of the AEC where the commission ends and the industry begins." Ribicoff would not be the only person to wonder about this. Until the 1979 accident at Three Mile Island forced the Nuclear Regulatory Commission to realize that it could not afford to be too friendly with the industry it was supposed to regulate, others, in government and without, were asking exactly the same question.

The contract may have seemed loose. Rickover's control over the operation was anything but. He exercised absolute control over Bettis, personally reading every document concerned with the project, mediating all disputes, settling all arguments. He also saw to it that no details of the project were left unchecked. He had the prototype models of the pressurized water reactor tested at the AEC's testing station in Idaho. He worried about how the reactor would fit into the submarine, how technicians would be able to maintain it, how engineers would deal with the various types of malfunctions that could be expected. "Rickover was a tyrant," said an engineer who worked for him at Bettis. "No Russian czar was more autocratic. He wanted everything checked out in advance. He didn't want any surprises—ever."

Rickover's rigorousness paid off. In 1948 Rickover amazed his fellow Navy officers by setting a target date—January 1, 1955—for the first nuclear submarine to put to sea. He was determined to meet it.

He and the men working with him knew that it was not going to be easy. The problems facing them were enormous. A metal had to be found to contain the uranium fuel, for example. Of the several tried, zirconium showed the best resistance to corrosion and the lowest affinity for neutrons. But it was also among the most expensive, costing half a million dollars a pound. Rickover did not let this deter him from using it. He prodded the U.S. Bureau of Mines to develop a less expensive method to produce zirconium. He prodded the scientists at Bettis to develop the alloy Zircaloy.[32]

He overcame other problems in much the same way. He pushed his staff to figure out a way to shield the reactor in order to protect the crew from radiation in the cramped quarters aboard a submarine. He pushed them to develop a drive system for the control rods. He pushed them to develop sealed-motor pumps to drive the high-pressure coolant water through the reactor while meeting the no-leak, limited-access, low-maintenance, and no-lubrication requirements he felt essential.

By mid-1953 the reactor was ready. Or, at least, the prototype was. And in a desert of Idaho, it was put through a simulated submerged crossing of the Atlantic and other tests. The submarine thermal reactor (STR) Mark I passed its tests with flying colors. The reactor went critical on March 30, 1953, and within a day showed itself capable of generating several thousand kilowatts of thermal energy. In June, the reactor was put through a hundred-hour run at full power. Completing it, the reactor showed not only that it was ready to be installed in a submarine but that it could produce large amounts of energy on a sustained basis.

Meanwhile, construction of the world's first nuclear submarine, named the *Nautilus* after the ship skippered by Captain Nemo in Jules Verne's *Twenty Thousand Leagues Under the Sea*, got under way at the Electric Boat shipyard in Groton, Connecticut. To Rickover's annoyance, the project did not meet its January 1 deadline. But it didn't miss it by much. On January 17, 1955, only seventeen days behind schedule, the *Nautilus* was at sea and sending back the message that heralded the dawn of a new age: "Under way on nuclear power."[33]

The *Nautilus*, in fact, was a striking success. On its shakedown cruise, everything—particularly the pressurized water reactor—

worked perfectly, and not just to drive the *Nautilus*. The nuclear submarine project produced more than a state-of-the-art undersea ship. It also produced a set of technical handbooks that pointed the way toward generating power by means of nuclear fission.

By the time the *Nautilus* was launched, the nation was already in the process of using these handbooks. Industrial groups had been growing impatient with the government monopoly on nuclear technology, and public-power enthusiasts were pushing the AEC for a civilian demonstration project. By the end of 1953, the AEC succumbed to the pressure and decided to go ahead and build the nation's first commercial nuclear power plant.

It had already been experimenting with different designs. In 1949 the AEC had authorized construction of Zinn's experimental breeder reactor (EBR) at the National Reactor Testing Station in Idaho. Construction got under way late that year on the small liquid metal–cooled fast-neutron breeder, and the machine was ready to test in 1951. A 100-kilowatt turbine was attached to it, and on December 20 the machine was started. It worked and became the first reactor to produce electric power in kilowatt quantities.

At Los Alamos, meanwhile, a group of researchers built a homogeneous-fuel reactor, which they called the "water boiler" because it was designed to use an aqueous solution of uranium salts. This small demonstration reactor worked well enough to persuade the AEC to authorize a larger one at Oak Ridge, which was completed and started up in 1952.

Other designs were also tested. By March of that year, some thirty-three reactors had either been operated, were operating, or were under construction in England, France, Canada, Norway, the U.S.S.R., and the U.S. Most of these were designed either to produce weapons-grade plutonium or to be used for research; few were intended to generate electric power.

The AEC wanted one that would. In 1953 the agency adopted the first plan designed to get one. It decided on a five-year, five-reactor program aimed at paving the way for private industry to get into the business of nuclear power. Included in the program, for which Congress approved a budget of $199 million, were plans for:

- A pressurized-water reactor, basically a large marine reactor adapted for land installation.
- A graphite-moderated, liquid-sodium-cooled reactor to be built north of Los Angeles in the Simi Mountains.

- A scaled-up version of the Oak Ridge homogeneous-fuel reactor.
- An experimental breeder reactor.
- An experimental boiling water reactor (BWR) in which water coolant would be allowed to boil in the reactor vessel, then piped directly into the turbine to generate electricity.

Competition among the different designs was fierce. Advocates of sodium-cooled reactors boasted of their efficiency at transferring heat from the core to water in a plant's steam generator. Backers of homogeneous-fuel reactors touted their design's inherent simplicity, reminding everyone that it was nothing but "a pipe, a pot and a pump." Breeder backers claimed that their design made the best use of uranium.[34]

One by one, though, the other designs dropped out of the running, leaving the field to the two so-called light-water designs, the pressurized water reactor (PWR) and the boiling water reactor. The operation of both these devices is quite similar. In both, a core of Zircaloy-clad fuel rods is activated by the withdrawal of graphite and boron control rods. In the PWR, heated water circulating around the fuel rods is pumped through a radioactive primary loop and into a steam generator. There it heats water that is used to produce steam, which is then harnessed to drive a turbine. In the boiling water reactor, the steam generator is eliminated, and the boiling water itself drives the turbine.

The design that won the competition was the BWR, which had proved itself experimentally. By the end of 1953, the AEC gave Rickover's group, which was already well into PWR design and which had a good working relationship with Westinghouse, the go-ahead to build the first commercial reactor as well.

Having decided to go ahead with the project, though, the AEC needed an industrial partner. It had little trouble finding one. The Duquesne Light and Power Company of Pittsburgh agreed to participate in the venture. It offered the AEC a site on the Ohio River at Shippingport. The AEC accepted and the project went ahead; Rickover and the Westinghouse team at Bettis designed and built the Shippingport Atomic Power Station while working on the submarine program.

Construction of the Shippingport reactor followed quickly after President Eisenhower's dramatic groundbreaking. In just over three years, the plant was complete. On December 2, 1957—fifteen years to the day after Fermi's group had achieved the first nuclear chain reaction at the University of Chicago—the Shippingport reactor went critical for the first time, generating 60 megawatts of electricity.[35]

Financially, its 60 megawatts came as no bargain. The cost of producing Shippingport's electricity was ten times higher than the prevailing price of power. But the plant was a technical success. Its completion and operation contributed enormously to the prestige of the AEC's Naval Reactors Branch and to that of its chief, Hyman Rickover. The reactor also served as a feather in the cap of the government's Atoms for Peace program and helped to establish light-water reactors as the machines of choice in the nuclear boom that followed Shippingport's construction.

But Shippingport's greatest contribution was psychological. The reactor showed that the atom could be harnessed for peaceful purposes and proved that the force that could destroy a city could also provide electric power for a city's population. Shippingport, both supporters and critics agreed, kept the promise that President Eisenhower had made at the United Nations.

But neither the opening of Shippingport nor the revisions of the Atomic Energy Act triggered an immediate response from private industry or sent utility company executives scurrying out in search of capital to finance plants of their own. What did were the 1957 Price-Anderson amendments to the Atomic Energy Act.

The amendments were important. They imposed a ceiling on the liability of any nuclear power licensee in the event of an accident at his plant—a ceiling that was, as it turned out, far lower than the likely costs of such an accident. The amendments established a $560 million fund to which the AEC and private insurers were to contribute. It also specified that once the $560 million was distributed, there was no further liability.[36]

Bitterly attacked by critics of the industry, the Price-Anderson amendments removed a major obstacle to the private development of nuclear power. With the obstacle removed, electric utilities quickly began to build and operate their own reactors. In 1957 the AEC issued two construction permits for commercial nuclear reactors. One went to Commonwealth Edison of Illinois to build a 200-megawatt boiling water reactor named Dresden 1 near Morris, Illinois. The other went to New York's Consolidated Edison Company so that it could begin construction of Indian Point 1, a 265-megawatt pressurized water reactor at Buchanan, twenty-six miles north of New York City on the Hudson River.

Utilities were not the only companies interested in nuclear power, though. In July 1959, the first American nuclear-powered ship, the *N.S. Savannah,* was launched at Camden, New Jersey. Later that same year, Dresden 1 received its operating license. Just over a year later, in November 1960, the first U.S.-designed nuclear reactor was started up overseas. Built by General Electric, the 16-megawatt boiling water reactor at Kahl, West Germany, was merely a demonstration project. But it was a successful one, and it helped to sell U.S. nuclear technology abroad.

Elsewhere around the U.S. and the nonsocialist world, nuclear power seemed to be catching on quickly. Plants, most of them built by either Westinghouse or General Electric, began to sprout up around the country like mushrooms after a rain. By the end of 1962, five privately owned reactors were in operation around the U.S., generating a total of just under 800 megawatts of electricity. By 1976 sixty reactors with a capacity of 43,000 megawatts were on-line in the U.S., while 146 more were on order, pushing both Westinghouse and GE to the forefront of the commercial nuclear business. The nuclear power boom forecast by scientific salesmen like Seaborg, Gamow, Dietz, and others seemed to have arrived. Nuclear power, a child of the Manhattan Project, seemed to have outgrown its lethal birth and matured into a useful citizen. Nuclear power appeared to have arrived. It also looked as if it were ready to stay.

Three

The Troubled Childhood

The appearance, however, was somewhat deceiving. Scientists and engineers had shown that it was possible to generate electricity using the power of the atom. What neither they nor the electric utilities had been able to show was that it was practical. For, what quickly became clear as the post-Korean conflict "nuclear boom" continued was that the people and firms involved—from the AEC to the electric utilities to the companies that actually built the reactors and power plants—were more interested in the idea of nuclear power than they were in its actual performance.

This became obvious in 1969 when California's Pacific Gas and Electric Company, the country's second largest private utility, announced plans to build a GE boiling water reactor at Bodega, the scenic seaside community in which director Alfred Hitchcock filmed his eerie thriller *The Birds*. The utility's announcement triggered an almost immediate protest by local residents and environmentalists, who had settled in Bodega because of its unspoiled beauty and who felt that the plant, with its huge concrete containment building, would spoil their view of the bay and its fishing fleet and desecrate one of the few pristine sites along California's rapidly developing coastline.[1]

Environmentalists thought that this was reason enough to oppose PG&E's plans. But they soon found an even better reason. The plant site—a low peninsula thrust out into the Pacific—was found to lie only a bit more than a mile from the line of the San Andreas Fault, the meeting place of two of the earth's major tectonic plates and the most active earthquake zone in the U.S. The fault is the line along which the Pacific plate, creeping slowly north and west on the earth's semimolten mantle, grinds against the more-or-less stationary North American plate. It is the occasional slippage of these plates, during which tremendous force is released, that causes the earthquakes that have plagued California, including the 1906 quake that leveled San Francisco.

The discovery that the plant site lay close to the San Andreas Fault did not seem to bother PG&E's enginners. They were confident that they could make the reactor earthquake-proof. In fact, company geologists insisted, the granite bedrock around the bay was solid; it had held firm during previous earthquakes and would do so again.

Their confidence was shaken, though, by one resident's recollection that during the 1906 quake, the peninsula upon which the reactor was to be built had rolled like the sea. It was further shaken when independent geologists found a new set of faults surrounding the plant and discovered that the land under the proposed site was not granite but a combination of silt, clay, and sand.[2]

Given these discoveries, the AEC had little choice but to act. In 1974 the commission's division of reactor licensing, whose approval was essential for all new reactors, withdrew its imprimatur and canceled the PG&E project.

The first cancellation in U.S. nuclear history, the PG&E fiasco might have been expected to produce a pause in the U.S.'s headlong drive to go nuclear. But U.S. utilities and nuclear plant builders took the cancellation in stride, barely hesitating before pressing on with their plans. GE's engineers dismissed the Bodega cancellation as an aberration rather than recognize it as a sign of problems to come. So did Westinghouse. Both companies were in the business of selling nuclear plants; neither was about to be deterred.

Indeed, GE all but ignored Bodega and pointed with pride to a project going on clear across the country in New Jersey. There at Oyster Creek, a stream that empties into Barnegat Bay on the Jersey shore, GE was building another plant.

Built for the Jersey Central Power and Light Company, the 650-megawatt Oyster Creek plant was a showpiece. Seen from the road, the plant site looked neat and efficient. The operation looked good on paper, too. Seeking to prove the economic viability of nuclear power, Jersey Central published a detailed cost breakdown of its new plant that made much of the fact that unlike Shippingport, it had been built entirely without federal subsidy. The utility also cited the construction of its plant as evidence that the age of commercially competitive nuclear power had dawned.

The dawn, however, was a false one, and both GE and Jersey Central knew it. The company could claim economic viability because it had not borne the full cost of building the Oyster Creek plant. The major share of the cost of building the plant had been borne by GE. The giant manufacturer, which made everything from power plants to toasters, had built Oyster Creek for $91 million on a "turnkey contract." This was a bargain-basement package deal covering equipment and construction, which the company made so economically attractive that, like people offered a deal they could not refuse by a mythical godfather, no American utility could turn it down. Oyster Creek was a "loss leader" designed to get American—and foreign—utilities hooked on nuclear power.[3]

The reason for such an approach was simple. The AEC and its contractor companies had made a major investment in developing reactor technology. In the five years preceding Oyster Creek's construction, the AEC had spent $1.2 billion; private companies, including GE, had invested about half that amount. Now the companies, at least, wanted to get their money back. Thirty or so reactor designs had been investigated by the AEC, but only two—Westinghouse's pressurized water reactor and GE's boiling water model—had been found to be really workable. The AEC had endorsed the two designs, given them its seal of approval. Now that it had, the companies wanted to make sure that their products became the industry's standards. They wanted to create and exploit a market for their machines.

For both GE and Westinghouse, the opportunity to do so could not have come at a better time. The early sixties had been a slow period for both companies. By 1964, the year that Oyster Creek was ordered, sales at Westinghouse had remained at $2 billion since 1957. GE had barely increased its sales of $5 billion during the same period. Morale at both companies was low and falling lower.

But both morale and sales quickly improved. In 1963 both companies got new management. Fred Borch, who had made his name selling light bulbs, took over as chief executive at GE. Donald Burnham, a veteran financial executive, took over the helm at Westinghouse.

Neither man lost any time getting his company moving. Adopting the slogan "Progress is our most important product," Borch decided to revitalize GE by putting the company's substantial resources into a series of high-risk ventures, all designed to appeal to the popular imagination—aerospace, computers, and, of course, nuclear power. Burnham, whose company faced the additional problem of being number two, Avis to GE's Hertz, decided to build Westinghouse's profits by branching out from the firm's traditional line of products. Within a short time, Westinghouse was involved with low-income housing, a car rental business, and a mail-order business. But the area in which Burnham placed his greatest hope was nuclear power. Taking advantage of the leg up that the company had gained by working with Rickover and the Navy on the *Nautilus* and Shippingport, Burnham dreamed of dominating the reactor market, not only in the U.S. but abroad as well.[4]

The competition between the companies was soon joined. GE engineers worked at full speed to design plants that were not only economically competitive with oil- or coal-fired plants, but so much cheaper that no utility executive would feel he could afford to pass them up. Westinghouse was just as determined to stay in the race. Convinced that construction costs would drop as the experience of building nuclear plants accumulated, GE decided to win widespread acceptance of its boiling water reactors by taking all the risks involved in their construction. This was why it offered to build Oyster Creek at an irresistible price. Westinghouse, no less competitive, offered similar packages and, in an effort to get ahead, speeded up the development of bigger and bigger reactors.

Utility companies, which had initially been slow to adopt the new technology, quickly found themselves convinced by the optimistic, most observers would say overoptimistic, cost projections put out by Westinghouse and GE. Foreign countries, some of which could ill afford nuclear plants and a few of which needed them about as badly as they needed a cholera epidemic, were soon caught up in the frenzy of interest in nuclear power. France, which was trying to develop its own reactor systems and, under the highly nationalistic leadership of the late Charles de Gaulle, avoid dependence upon the U.S. and its monopoly of uranium enrichment technology, held off from ordering. But other countries lined up to buy U.S.-built light-water reactors. By the close of 1966, GE and Westinghouse had six orders each to build a dozen plants in Switzerland, Spain, India, Belgium,

Germany, Sweden, and Japan. They had already built twenty-one plants in the U.S.

By the midsixties, GE was clearly ahead in the race for domination of the nuclear power field. The first company to publish an actual price list, GE also moved ahead of Westinghouse in increasing the sizes of plants. Following a period in which the largest plant built had generated a mere 200 megawatts, GE had forced the pace of the race by building Oyster Creek at 650 megawatts. A year later, keeping up with the increasing size of coal-fired plants, GE offered buyers an 800-megawatt model, followed a year later by an even larger plant, an 1,100-megawatt giant.

But what really put GE ahead in the race was the coup it scored in 1966 when it sold a reactor to the nation's largest producer of electricity, the Tennessee Valley Authority. Located right in the heart of some of the nation's most productive coal country, the publicly owned TVA generated most of its power by either burning the locally mined coal or by harnessing the power of major rivers like the Tennessee and other southern streams. It had no real need to go nuclear, but decided to do so to enhance its image as a progressive, forward-looking operation. It did not, however, intend to go nuclear at a premium. Proud of its record of providing a great deal of power at low cost, the TVA made it clear that anyone who sold it a reactor would have to sell it cheaply.

Both GE and Westinghouse rose to the TVA's challenge. But GE won the competition. It offered the TVA a fixed price of $250 million for each of two 1,000-megawatt plants to be built at Browns Ferry, Alabama. The price was a good one. GE's price came out to be $116 per kilowatt of generating capacity. This put it $5 a kilowatt below the Westinghouse bid of $121. Even more startling, it put it $1 a kilowatt below the lowest coal plant bid of $117.

Nor was low cost per kilowatt the only thing GE offered to win the TVA contract. The company not only guaranteed the performance of its uranium fuel but offered to pay TVA a penalty of $1,500 for each hour of peak demand that the plant failed to function according to contract. TVA modified the deal slightly. In keeping with its practice of designing its own projects, the authority turned down GE's proposal for a turnkey plant and accepted instead a fixed-price deal on equipment along with guarantees that it would perform as promised.[5]

The news media hailed the TVA decision to go nuclear as the start of a new era in electric generation. But the media were not alone in their enthusiasm. Utility companies and their executives joined in the chorus, predicting that costs would actually come down with the building of each successive nuclear power plant and forecasting that the price of uranium would also drop as the construction of more and more plants created a major market for the nuclear fuel.

There seemed at the time to be at least some basis for this prediction. In 1964 President Lyndon Johnson signed an amendment to the Atomic Energy Act that provided for the eventual private ownership of nuclear fuel. Prior to the passage of the amendment, the government had owned all nuclear fuel and leased it to the industry. The amendment allowed the utilities themselves to buy and own uranium and to have it enriched by the AEC for a fee.

But neither the TVA contract nor the amendment to the Atomic Energy Act, which the AEC put into effect in 1969, were enough to convince one dissenter. Philip Sporn, former chief of the huge American Electric Power Company, had never been convinced by the zealots that nuclear power was economical. In 1967 he aired his suspicions by producing a detailed analysis of the GE bid for Oyster Creek. His analysis showed convincingly that the claim that cost-competitive nuclear power had arrived was . . . well, premature. Noting the competition between the two reactor-building companies, he dismissed the nuclear boom of the midsixties as "The Great Bandwagon Market," citing with particular scorn the fact that when the TVA sought bids for a third nuclear plant, GE's bargain price was no longer available. Clearly, said Sporn, the GE bid on Browns Ferry had been a "come-on," and a successful one at that.[6]

Sporn's study shook the industry. As former chief of the world's largest privately owned utility and as a man with a reputation for running his company efficiently, Sporn could hardly be suspected of knee-jerk opposition to nuclear power. Nor could Sporn's three main points be ignored. They were that the utility industry and the government had become so caught up in their enthusiasm for the atom that they had forgotten that the costs of such "conventional" fuels as coal and oil were actually going down, that the real costs of building nuclear plants were 10 to 15 percent higher than those estimated by the electric companies, and that the actual cost of producing nuclear electricity once plants were built would be 20 percent or more higher than originally estimated.

Sporn's points were not ignored. But his warning was. He cautioned that "nuclearization" of the power industry was proceeding too quickly, with construction getting ahead of engineering in many areas. And he urged the industry to slow down and allow the technology of nuclear generation to develop properly before committing itself to it.

Both the electric companies and the AEC rejected Sporn's analysis of the situation, indicating that they found the grand old man of electric power generation too conservative for their tastes. The bandwagon was rolling, and a great many people—in the AEC, in the utility industry, in the corporate offices of GE and Westinghouse—had a vested interest in keeping it moving.

Even Sporn's old company jumped aboard. Donald Cook, who had become president of American Electric Power on Sporn's retirement in 1961, found himself convinced that there was "a great future in nuclear power." Determined to change the image of utility company executives as stuffy and old-fashioned, he had impressed both the press and his fellow executives with his view that power could be delivered more cheaply. He had also impressed President Johnson to the point that the Chief Executive had offered him a cabinet post.

AEP owned or had access to enormous amounts of coal, much of it temptingly close to its plants. But Cook ignored this resource. Illinois's Commonwealth Edison announced that it would soon be 40 percent nuclear. Detroit Edison was building a breeder reactor. New England Utilities ordered nuclear plants. Companies all across the U.S. were going nuclear.

Cook could not remain on the sidelines. In 1967 he ordered two reactors, and followed a company practice by naming them for himself—Cook 1 and Cook 2. The purchase proved no bargain. By the time the plants, plagued by construction delays, got on-line, by the time AEP had finished paying for the electricity it was forced to buy from other utilities to meet demand during construction, they ended up costing three times the original estimate.[7]

The problem, of course, was one of timing. Like a surfer who just misses the crest of a wave, Cook got AEP into the nuclear business just a wee bit late. It was the companies that bought early that got the good deals. AEP placed its orders after GE and Westinghouse, acknowledging that turnkey projects were not making them any money, had stopped offering fixed price bids. By then, too, the electrical titans were no longer alone in the reactor-building business. Both Babcock and Wilcox and Combustion Engineering, which had been known primarily as boiler makers, had diversified and gotten into the reactor game, selling pressurized water reactors of their own design. By the end of the decade, operational nuclear plants were generating 4,200 megawatts of electricity. But plants capable of generating a total of 72,000 megawatts were either on order or actually under construction.

No question about it, business was booming. GE and Westinghouse were both doing well. Combustion Engineering and Babcock and Wilcox were getting enough orders to justify their decision to diversify and build reactors. But this did not mean that the outlook for nuclear power was unclouded. The industry, which many critics felt was growing too fast for its own health, was beginning to suffer growth pains.

Part of the problem involved scale. The great boom in nuclear plant orders occurred when none of the plants in operation was bigger than 200 megawatts. It generated orders for plants in the 500-megawatt range. But these orders quickly escalated into orders for even bigger plants. All of the new orders received by GE, Westinghouse, Babcock and Wilcox, and Combustion Engineering were for plants of 1,000 megawatts or more.

Building the big plants proved more difficult than the companies had anticipated. As every engineer knows, scaling up a design involves far more than merely making everything bigger. The bigger plants were subject to greater pressures and greater strains. They required more elaborate safety devices and more reliable emergency core-cooling systems (ECCS), the huge networks of pipes designed to dump tons—a veritable Niagara—of water into their scaled-up cores in the event of a dreaded LOCA, or loss-of-coolant accident. Without such systems, the fissile uranium in the core would rapidly overheat and could, if the heating were not stopped and reversed, quite literally melt its way through the reactor vessel.

GE, Westinghouse, and the others soon found that there were few economies of scale when it came to building nuclear power plants. A 1,000-megawatt plant did not cost twice as much as a 500-megawatt installation. Often, it cost three or four times as much.[8]

The economics of nuclear power was not the only problem confronting the AEC and the nuclear industry during the boom years of the sixties. The industry's growth itself was a problem.

Outwardly, no one involved with the atom expressed anything but confidence. Glenn Seaborg, who was not only the "granddaddy of plutonium," but, by his own description, "the nation's number-one salesman for the atom," continued to see the nuclear future through rose-colored glasses. In 1964, while heading the U.S. delegation to the United Nations Conference on the Peaceful Uses of Atomic Energy in Geneva, Switzerland, Seaborg painted a bright picture of the atom's prospects. "As we look at the status of nuclear energy development, we see something solid," he said. "We find that quietly, without fanfare, the thing we have been waiting for has happened: the age of nuclear power has begun." A short time later, attending the General Conference of the International Atomic Energy Agency in Vienna, he hailed the progress that had been made in nuclear technology, claiming that "the time has arrived when we have the capability of producing nuclear power economically," and predicting that as many as half the power plants ordered in the U.S. in the coming decade would be nuclear.[9]

Seaborg's assessment of U.S. interest in nuclear power was accurate. U.S. utilities were actively considering a major move to nuclear plants, and the American public seemed equally excited. The majority of Americans saw the atom, which was propelling submarines and generating electricity, as a friendly little fellow, a beneficial cousin of Reddy Kilowatt, the cartoon figure that U.S. electric companies used to help sell their product. Except for the handful of local residents who had objected—and not all that loudly, either—to construction of nuclear plants near their homes, few had actively opposed nuclear power. In fact, the only serious opposition to nuclear power had surfaced in 1969 when PG&E had first announced plans to build its Bodega Bay plant.

But the AEC was concerned about opposition to its overall program. Regarding itself as the nation's principal promoter of nuclear power more than the regulator of the nuclear industry, the AEC sought to avoid controversy whenever possible and to minimize it when it could not be avoided.

One of the ways it did this was through the structure of its hearing procedures. The Atomic Energy Act of 1954 required the AEC to hold a public hearing before it could issue a permit to construct a nuclear plant. The law also gave local residents who objected to the proposed plant the opportunity to be heard. As set up by the law, the hearings were formal legal proceedings; all the parties involved, from the utility company seeking the permit to the AEC and its staff to the intervenors who objected to the plant, were represented by attorneys. The AEC could not dispense with the hearings, but in order to prevent them from slowing the nuclearization of America, it designed a set of rules and procedures designed to speed up the process.

The procedures were simple. Prior to the hearing, the AEC staff met with the utility company to work out any differences so that none needed to be aired before the hearing board. The hearing board, a three-member body whose members were selected by the AEC, had strictly limited powers. Its assigned role was solely to determine whether the proposed plans conformed to established AEC policy. The board did not carry out its own independent evaluation of the plant or the utility's application. Nor were challengers able to make their opposition effective. Local residents opposed to a proposed nuclear plant rarely possessed either the resources or the technical expertise to determine if the plant in question was safe or properly designed. The AEC was hardly about to provide such information. Under its own rules, it declined to grant opponents access to its own data, even where potential safety problems were concerned.

This attitude was particularly prevalent under Seaborg, who served as the AEC's principal adviser through the late forties and as Presidential Science Adviser in the fifties. Seaborg became chairman of the AEC in 1961 and immediately began to use his position to push the programs he was convinced were best for the U.S. Seaborg believed that the U.S. should have nuclear power. He had little patience with anyone who disagreed.

Seaborg, in fact, was an elitist. He believed that scientists, especially physicists, knew more than the man in the street, and that Nobel Prize winners, of which he happened to be one, knew more than other physicists. His attitude, said AEC historian Richard Hewlett, could best be summed up by the title of a popular television program. The "granddaddy of plutonium" believed that "Father Knows Best." And Seaborg never had any doubt as to who "Father" was. He did not doubt or question for a moment who should make the decisions about the construction or licensing of nuclear power plants. As far as Seaborg was concerned, that responsibility rested squarely with the AEC and even more squarely with its chairman.

As far as Seaborg was also concerned, the AEC was fully qualified to fulfill that responsibility. But, critics countered, Seaborg's opinion of the AEC was somewhat inflated. The AEC was a managerial mess, with little in the way of centralized control. During the late fifties and early sixties, the congressional Joint Committee on

Atomic Energy had gradually assumed the role as the major developer of nuclear energy in the U.S. In the process, the traditional line separating the powers of the legislative (JCAE) and executive (AEC) branches of government became blurred. As critics saw it, in adopting the role of cheerleader, the AEC had abandoned its role of watchdog. In becoming the chief promoter of the nuclear power industry, the commission apparently forgot that it also had an obligation to see that the industry grew responsibly and with a proper regard for the safety of the people it was supposed to serve.

The paternalistic attitude of the JCAE was obvious in its attitudes toward environmentalists and others who, though hardly enemies of nuclear power, certainly had questions about its development. Witnesses who appeared before the JCAE complained that their questions were treated with a jovial contempt. Informed critics noted that the JCAE seemed totally uninterested in the health dangers posed by the testing of nuclear weapons in the Nevada desert.* Nor did the JCAE seem interested in the deaths of uranium miners, who suffered unduly from the radioactive effects of the ore they were working so hard to extract from the earth.[10]

So enthusiastic was the JCAE, in fact, that it promoted a number of projects that even nuclear enthusiasts considered ill-advised, most notably the nuclear-powered plane, an idea that, fortunately and quite literally, never got off the ground.

The attitudes and actions of the AEC were equally questionable. During the late fifties and early sixties, the commission continued to work closely with those industrial companies and university researchers that had been involved with the Manhattan Project, fostering the idea of the existence of a sort of "nuclear club." During the boom years, AEC contracts continued to go to members of the same group, which included General Electric, Union Carbide, Sandia Laboratories (a subsidiary of Western Electric Company), Bendix, Du Pont, and the Universities of California and Chicago.

To call the arrangement advantageous to the companies would be to understate the situation. The contracts conferred the obvious direct advantages to the firms to which they were awarded, of course. But they also gave them an invaluable opportunity to develop the

---

*In early 1984 federal courts held that the U.S. government was indeed responsible for failing to adequately protect residents of southern Utah from the fallout resulting from these tests and was thus responsible for several cancer deaths among people in the area.

kind of nuclear expertise that could later be put to good commercial use. This experience, it turned out, could be gained in no other way; nuclear technology was, after all, a government monopoly.

Attitude, however, was only one of the problems facing the developing Atomic Energy Commission. Organization, or the lack thereof, presented the agency with another set of problems. From its founding, the AEC's operational work was handled through field and area offices, not from a central office. The system as set up by the AEC's first general manager had put "operations offices" in New York; Chicago; Richland, Washington; Los Alamos, New Mexico; and Oak Ridge, Tennessee. Additional offices were later opened in Las Vegas to oversee the Nevada test site, in Idaho Falls to manage the AEC's reactor testing facility, in San Francisco, and in Savannah River, Georgia.

The plethora of offices gave the AEC a healthy share of managerial headaches. As the decade of the seventies got under way, the AEC found itself with some 4,000 people in its various field offices, another 2,000 in Washington. The agency's regulatory arm, located in the District of Columbia, employed another 2,000 people. And most of the commission's actual nuclear work was still done by the more than 100,000 employees who worked for the AEC's 200-odd contractors. The AEC, critics charged, was so busy promoting nuclear power and trying to manage its widespread network of field offices that it had little time to be concerned about the question of nuclear plant safety.[11]

The charge was not wholly unjustified. The AEC was concerned with nuclear safety. It simply did not see any need, at least immediately, to share this concern with the public.

Initially at least, the AEC simply assumed that nuclear reactors were safe. The problem of reactor safety was barely mentioned in Seaborg's 1962 report to President John F. Kennedy; the safety issue took up less than a full page of the one-hundred-page report.[12] It is not hard to understand why. In the process of preparing the report, the AEC discussed the safety question with the Department of the Interior, the Federal Power Commission, and the Bureau of the Budget. It discussed safety with the strongly pronuclear Joint Committee on Atomic Energy and the Atomic Industrial Forum, the nuclear power industry's trade organization. It did not, though, seek the input of the only official body specifically charged with promoting nuclear plant safety—the AEC's own Advisory Committee on Reactor Safety.

The omission was unfortunate. In the years since the development of the first nuclear reactors, the committee had recognized a number of safety problems, most of them involving the accidental loss of reactor coolant and the resultant overheating of the reactor core. The 1962 report, however, mentioned none of these problems. It declared simply that vigorous efforts should continue to be made to maximize "the inherent safety of nuclear power."

Seaborg himself studiously avoided any public discussion of nuclear plant risks. When asked, he dismissed questions with the statement that plants were safe, that safety was one of the commission's principal considerations, and that everything possible was being done to protect the public. The commission itself followed Seaborg's lead. Both formally and informally, it delegated responsibility for making nuclear plants safe to the nuclear power industry. The industry, for its part, insisted that it took every possible precaution, though Alvin Weinberg, who helped design the original pressurized water reactor, questions that claim. The industry, he maintains, could not take every possible precaution and still keep its reactors competitive with fossil-fuel plants. There was, said Weinberg, a basic conflict between the need to make plants as safe as possible and the need to make them as cheap as possible. Given the obvious need to make nuclear power as cheap as power from coal-fired plants, he says, safety was given a rather low priority.

At least most of the time. Many companies sought to cut the costs of transmitting power from remote sites by seeking to locate nuclear power plants as close as possible to the urban centers that would be using the power they generated. Though such a siting policy increased the number of people who might be exposed to nuclear radiation in the event of an accident, Seaborg was willing to meet the industry at least halfway. Reversing its initial siting policy, the AEC did allow nuclear plants to be built close to some metropolitan areas. It did not, though, go as far as New York's Consolidated Edison wanted it to go. Con Ed asked for permission to build a nuclear power plant in the Ravenswood section of Queens, just across the East River from midtown Manhattan. Con Ed did not seem overly concerned with the fact that 5.5 million people lived or worked within five miles of the plant site. The AEC, however, was, and denied Con Ed its permit. Other plants, meanwhile, were allowed to go ahead.[13]

This does not mean, though, that the AEC considered an accident at a nuclear power plant an impossibility. Even the industry had acknowledged that although accidents were unlikely, they were possible. Charles Weaver, vice president of Westinghouse, had admitted as much when he testified before the JCAE in 1956 and conceded that the industry could not "exclude the possibility that a great enough fool aided by a great enough conspiracy could bring about an accident exceeding available insurance."[14] His statement, combined with those of other representatives of the nuclear industry that rather than accept bankrupting liabilities they would abandon nuclear power, prompted the JCAE to ask the AEC for an evaluation of the risks of a major reactor accident. The AEC in turn asked its Brookhaven National Laboratory to conduct such a study and come up with an answer to the JCAE's question.

The result of the Brookhaven investigation, sent to the commission in 1957, was a document bearing the less than exciting title *Theoretical Possibilities and Consequences of Major Accidents in Large Nuclear Power Plants* and known from its AEC publication number as "WASH-740." The study concerned a hypothetical reactor located some thirty miles upwind of a major city (Con Ed's Indian Point plant fit the hypothetical description exactly) that had undergone an accident and released a major fraction of its radioactive material into the air, where it was carried across the countryside by winds. In their "worst case" scenario, the Brookhaven researchers estimated that such an accident would kill some 3,400 people, injure another 43,000, and cause $7 billion in property damage. The Brookhaven study emphasized that its scenario was not a prediction; it was merely a deliberately pessimistic evaluation of what could happen in an accident that nuclear technology made possible, though not very probable.[15]

The nuclear power industry had been concerned about lawsuits before publication of the Brookhaven study. The publication of WASH-740 intensified its concern. It also intensified the concern of both the JCAE and the AEC, which together successfully pushed for the passage of the 1957 Price-Anderson amendments to the Atomic Energy Act. But the Brookhaven study did not eliminate uncertainty about nuclear safety. This uncertainty, in fact, increased as the nuclear boom continued and as reactors, originally manageable machines of 200 megawatts or so, began to evolve into the 1,000-megawatt machines that seemed destined to become the industry's standard. Larger reactors, the AEC's safety advisers insisted, had to be more complicated—and hence potentially more dangerous—than their smaller cousins.

The reason for this was not hard to understand. Larger reactors would by their very nature have larger cores containing larger amounts of uranium. These larger cores would not only tend to overheat more rapidly in the event of loss-of-coolant accidents, but tend to hold their heat longer. Such reactors would also contain more radioactive material than smaller machines. Cooling them would require not only more plumbing, but more intricate plumbing; and more complex machines would, naturally, be more likely to malfunction than simpler devices with fewer parts. In fact, said AEC safety experts, larger reactors would be far more likely than smaller machines to undergo a series of events that could culminate in a unique problem called a "meltdown." Such an event, said engineers, could occur if the core of a large reactor became uncovered as a result of coolant loss, and overheated. Unless the core was cooled quickly, its temperature would climb rapidly and its uranium fuel would melt and become a heavy, white-hot mass that would melt its way through the reactor vessel, drop into the basement of the plant, and then melt its way into the ground. Unless it encountered water, said safety experts, the core could theoretically melt its way "clear through to China."[16]

The AEC was not insensitive to the risks involved in what quickly became known as "the China Syndrome." In fact, the safety problems associated with large reactors were examined in a study that the AEC launched in secret during the summer of 1964. Headed by Clifford Beck of the AEC's regulatory staff, the new study was intended to be an update of WASH-740. It was also intended to calm slowly rising public fears that reactors were unsafe. AEC internal documents indicate that the agency hoped that the new estimates of accident consequences would be lower than those in WASH-740, a finding that would constitute a public relations bonus for the agency.

AEC documents also indicate that there were some internal conflicts over the study. Some agency insiders wanted to conduct a no-holds-barred study, ignoring any public relations considerations and letting the facts developed during the course of their research speak for themselves. But others felt that such a study was far too sensitive to be done in such a manner. Nothing, they felt, should be allowed to undermine the public's increasingly shaky confidence in nuclear plant safety. "Great care should be exercised in any revision to avoid establishing and/or reinforcing the popular notion that reactors are unsafe," wrote S. Allan Lough, a member of the study's steering committee. "Though this is a public information or promotional problem that the AEC now faces with less than desirable success, I feel that by calculating the consequences of hypothetical accidents the AEC should not place itself in the position of making the location of reactors near urban areas nearly indefensible."[17]

The Brookhaven scientists worked on the study through the summer and fall of 1964. The findings in WASH-740 were based on a hypothetical accident in a 150-megawatt reactor. The Brookhaven group based its second study on an accident in a 1,000-megawatt installation, and came up with a quite different set of numbers. They calculated that as many as 45,000 people might be killed in a major reactor accident, and estimated that the property damage might be as much as forty times greater than the $7 billion figure found in the 1957 study. Indeed, as one Brookhaven researcher told the study's steering committee, the possible size of the area contaminated in such a hypothetical disaster might be equal to that of the state of Pennsylvania—45,333 square miles.

Predictably, the steering committee was stunned by the results. It urged the Brookhaven team to review its research to see if it might have overlooked any factors that might mitigate the impact of such an accident. It also asked the researchers to consider whether more sophisticated methods of calculating the consequences of an accident might yield lower estimates.

The researchers were unable to oblige the committee. They rechecked their calculations, then told the committee that they had found in their study "nothing inherent in reactors or in safeguard systems as they now have been developed which guarantees either that major reactor accidents will not occur or that protective safeguard systems will not fail." Said the Brookhaven team: "Should such accidents occur and the protective systems fail, very large damages could result."

The findings of the Brookhaven group led to a full-scale debate within the study's steering committee. Some members worried that publication of the results would strengthen the antinuclear forces and set back the AEC's plans to build and license more nuclear plants, including some sited near urban areas. They wanted data suggesting that accidents such as those postulated by the Brookhaven team were "incredible events," whose chances of actually occurring were so small as to be nonexistent. Their attitude was attacked as unscientific by other members of the committee and by members of the study team. Dr. Clifford Beck, head of the steering committee, tried himself to write a chapter on accident probability. But after preparing several drafts, he was forced to admit that he could arrive at no technically defensible estimate of the chances of a serious accident. Reactor technology was complicated, he admitted, and as a result, even seemingly minor problems could cause serious consequences. "[M]inor events in themselves, in combination with other abnormalities, can turn an insignificant situation into a major accident," he wrote. "Reactor technology is still in a relatively early stage of development and it is not yet certain that all possibilities of unsafe behavior have been identified and properly safeguarded." Beck concluded, in short, that it was possible to predict what would happen in the event of an accident. But it was all but impossible to estimate the likelihood that such an accident would occur.

The deadlock over the Brookhaven conclusions threw more than just the study group into turmoil. The steering committee was reluctant to publish any report that might strengthen the opposition to nuclear power. So the committee members passed the buck along to AEC Chairman Seaborg. He would have to decide how to present the study to the JCAE and work with the committee to decide where to take it from there.

The commission's decision was not long in coming. Early in 1965 the steering committee met privately with representatives of the Atomic Industrial Forum, the nuclear industry's lobbying group, to which draft copies of the updated version of WASH-740 had already been circulated. Asking for more time to study the report, the industry spokesmen asked Beck if more emphasis could not be placed on the low probability that an accident such as that described could actually take place. When Beck explained the problem encountered in estimating probabilities, the meeting ended inconclusively.[18]

The AEC took up the Brookhaven study itself in May of that year, at a meeting during which the commissioners decided to hold private talks with the JCAE in order to decide how to handle the study. The following month the commissioners met privately with Congressman Chet Holifield of California, chairman of the JCAE. The commissioners wondered if Holifield might prefer instead a report on the safety systems that the industry was developing to prevent accidents, rather than an updated version of WASH-740. But still, it was the AEC that finally decided what to do with the report. Given the AIF's opposition to its publication, as well as the probable impact of making such a report public, the agency decided to withhold it. Instead of releasing the scientists' scary findings, Seaborg sent the JCAE a letter noting that the reactors then being built were larger than those considered for construction in 1957, and stating that in the kinds of hypothetical accidents that might occur, "the theoretically calculated damages would not be less and under some circumstances would be substantially more than the consequences reported in the earlier study." Seaborg recognized that this conclusion accentuated the need to protect the industry through the Price-Anderson amendments. What he did not recognize was the need for stricter safety regulations by his own agency, which was charged by law not merely with helping to develop the nuclear industry, but with protecting the public health and safety in the process.

Word of the Brookhaven study was not long in leaking out. But the AEC responded to queries about the study by saying only that it had never been completed. Its answer satisfied all but the most ardent antinuclear types, and the absence of findings as frightening as those compiled by the Brookhaven team allowed the on-again-off-again nuclear bandwagon to resume rolling. Few of those who knew of the existence of the study, from Seaborg and the AEC commissioners to the members and staff of the JCAE to the leaders of the nuclear industry to the people who had actually compiled it, said anything about it during the years that followed its completion. And the AEC took advantage of the silence to issue construction permits for some thirty large nuclear power plants, facilities to be built close to such urban centers as Boston, New York, Chicago, and Miami. Blithely maintaining that these plants could operate without "undue risk" to the health and safety of the public, the AEC, and Seaborg in particular, took it for granted that sufficient safety systems would be developed by the time the plants in question were ready to operate. The commission had been given an opportunity to put public safety first among its considerations. More eager to promote nuclear power than to assure safety, the AEC let the opportunity slip by, and in so doing, threw away its chance to win public trust and confidence. It would not soon get another.[19]

Four

A Difficult Adolescence

Developmental psychologists have divided human life into stages—infancy, childhood, adolescence, adulthood. The life of the nuclear power industry has followed a similar pattern. The industry's birth, an outgrowth of the often frenetic efforts of both the U.S. government and its scientists to bring World War II to a speedy end, was somewhat premature. Commercial nuclear power was not exactly "untimely ripp'd" like Shakespeare's Macduff from the womb of its Manhattan Project mother. But it was certainly born before it was fully developed and thrust out into the world before it was fully viable. Helped along by the Atomic Energy Commission, which served as its self- as well as court-appointed guardian, and by the congressional Joint Committee on Atomic Energy, which served as its enthusiastic godfather, the industry managed to survive the childhood diseases of overly rapid development and standardization of equipment, of noncompetitive prices, of newness. Strongly—some would say too strongly—supported by those determined to push its progress, it made it through infancy and a troubled childhood. Still benefiting from the expert management that characterized the AEC's Naval Reactors program, the industry emerged from the decade of the fifties with the confidence that it could build and operate small reactors, like those at Shippingport, Pennsylvania, Rowe, Massachusetts, and other locations. Essentially slightly scaled-up versions of the pressurized water reactors used to power the *Nautilus* and other nuclear submarines, these early reactors, all of which generated 200 megawatts of electricity or less, were small enough to be manageable and simple enough to be safe. Indeed, most of these early reactors have operated safely and efficiently since they first went on-line, providing their owners and consumers with safe, dependable power, even when they have not succeeded in providing large amounts of it inexpensively.

The industry entered the decade of the sixties in good shape, although with an unjustifiable confidence in its ability to expand its capacity and improve its economics simply by making newer reactors bigger. But as the decade approached its midpoint, it became clear that the industry's optimism was ungrounded. The U.S. nuclear power industry had not outgrown the problems of its first decade; it had merely delayed dealing with them.

The first sign that the industry had not dealt with its problems came in April 1965. What provided it was the decision by Chicago's Commonwealth Edison Company to ask the AEC for permission to build another nuclear power plant in Morris, next to the Dresden 1 plant that the company had been operating there since 1960. Dresden 1 was a small plant, with a capacity of a mere 207 megawatts. Dresden 2, with a capacity of 794 megawatts, was to be almost four times as large. Nor was Commonwealth the only company looking toward expanding the size of its plants. Before the end of that year, New York's Consolidated Edison Company sought permission to build a new plant next to its Indian Point 1 facility, whose 150-megawatt capacity made it one of the industry's small fry. At 873 megawatts, Indian Point 2 would not only be six times as large as its sister plant, it would be the largest plant yet considered for licensing.

Other firms soon followed suit. Early in 1966 the Tennessee Valley Authority sought construction permits for the Browns Ferry Nuclear Power Station near Decatur, Alabama. Its application gave the industry a new subject to discuss when it talked about size. Each of the two reactors at Browns Ferry, to be named Sequoyah 1 and 2, was to have a capacity of 1,148 megawatts and dwarf both the Con Ed and Com Ed reactors.[1]

Ever the enthusiast, AEC Chairman Glenn Seaborg hailed the almost exponential increase in reactor size as evidence that nuclear plant design was sound and proof that the industry was coming of age. The industry echoed Seaborg's encomiums, singing paeans of praise to itself.

But enthusiasm for the new plants was anything but unqualified. The AEC's Advisory Committee on Reactor Safeguards wondered whether it ought to send the commission a letter warning it about the safety problems posed by such large plants. The ACRS's quandary should not have been necessary; the committee's responsibility—to review and make recommendations on the safety of each proposed plant—was clear. But the ACRS's record was ambiguous. The committee had, after all, concurred in, or at least raised no objections to, the suppression of its updated version of WASH-740. Nor had it objected when AEC Director of Regulation Harold Price had warned it that the overly candid expression of its views on safety could create public relations problems for the AEC or embarrass the industry of which it had appointed itself guardian.[2]

What happened, then, when the applications for the three new plants came before the ACRS was that the committee held a closed-door meeting. There it noted that, while the safety problems that were supposed to be solved during the construction of the plants were still far from solution, the AEC had continued to issue permits in the expectation that they would be. The ACRS had been willing to go along, at least in part, because all of the plants built to date had been sited well away from urban centers and other densely populated areas. What concerned ACRS committee members now was that a large plant was about to be built on the very edge of one of the country's major population concentrations. Close to 20 million people, an amount equal to about 10 percent of the entire population of the U.S., lived within a fifty-mile radius of the site at which Con Ed proposed to build Indian Point 2.[3]

It was unfair, as engineers later did, to refer to Buchanan, New York, where Indian Point 2 was eventually built, and which lay to the north of such commuter communities as Hastings-on-Hudson and Croton-on-Hudson, as "Hiroshima-on-Hudson." There was absolutely no chance that the plant could explode like the bomb that destroyed the Japanese city. But it was not unreasonable to worry about what might happen if the plant suffered a loss-of-coolant accident. A meltdown, ACRS engineers all recognized, could result in the release of large amounts of radioactivity from the plant and could expose millions of people to its effects.

Scientists at both the ACRS and the AEC's Brookhaven Laboratory had figured as much during their work aimed at updating WASH-740. Their results, though, remained a secret and had not even been compiled for internal use. But there was no secret, at least within the AEC, about the engineers' concerns. The commission had gone along with some of these concerns and had required the installation of emergency core-cooling systems, or ECCS, on all of the large new reactors (they were not required on the older, smaller reactors). But those concerned with safety wanted the commission to go even further and require some new safety systems—most notably a water-filled sump, or "core catcher," to hold and cool an overheated reactor core before it could melt its way through the containment and into the ground. The commission was not sure about the necessity for such a device. The industry, however, was. It did not believe that such a backup was necessary at all.

In the spring of 1965, the ACRS composed a letter warning against siting reactors near population centers, sent it to Seaborg, and then met with the AEC chairman to discuss it. The committee's attitude confronted the commission with a problem. As Price saw it, declaring that a reactor was not safe enough to build near a metropolitan area would make people wonder if it was safe enough to build anywhere. In particular, it would make people in the area to which the reactor was to be relocated justifiably curious as to why the reactor was suddenly considered safe enough to put in their backyards. The ACRS letter was not made public. Worse, it was clearly branded as unwelcome. On this occasion, as on others, the ACRS was told that the commission would prefer not to receive its unfavorable reports on reactor safety.

Anything but encouraged, the ACRS pressed ahead with its review of Indian Point 2, sending the commission a public report that can best, or most charitably, be described as "vague." It suggested that the emergency core-cooling system designed for the plant could be improved during construction and implied that the proposed reactor could probably be operated at the site without "undue risk." A private report, transmitted to the AEC a day later, however, told a different story. Going into some detail about the possibilities of malfunctions at the plant, it said quite categorically that additional precautions should be taken with Indian Point 2, and said that unless they were, reactors of similar size and design should not be built near heavily populated areas.[4]

To say that Seaborg was unhappy with the letter would be to put it mildly. Warning that such communications could have a serious and adverse impact on the industry, Seaborg simply tabled the letter. The ACRS could have sent the letter and released it anyway. But it did not. In its own way as much a part of the pronuclear team as Seaborg, it did not want to take any action that might result in a moratorium on nuclear power plant construction. Instead, it soldiered on, offering the commission its advice confidentially. The commission accepted the ACRS's advice in confidence—and just as confidentially ignored it.

The commission had plenty of support in its action. The Joint Committee on Atomic Energy had found the committee's concerns querulous and had accused it of standing in the way of the federal government's program for getting "kilowatts to the people." Congressman Craig Hosmer of California, the JCAE's senior Republican member, won applause at a nuclear industry gathering by attacking the ACRS's "lopsided" emphasis on safety and declaring that it was adversely affecting the economics of nuclear power.[5]

The ACRS and its researchers were a thorn in the side of the AEC. Their studies, including one conducted in Idaho in which a scaled-down, specially built reactor was actually allowed to melt down in order to determine what exactly would happen in such an accident, failed to provide the AEC, the JCAE, and the industry with the evidence to prove their assurances that reactors were safe and accidents unlikely. Instead, they suggested exactly the opposite: that the AEC was too deep into its role as nuclear cheerleader to notice that there were serious problems in the design and construction of a growing number of nuclear power plants.

The Idaho tests, run during the winter of 1970 and 1971, were, in fact, particularly discouraging. Performed on a teakettle-sized scale model of a pressurized water reactor, they showed that nuclear plant design, especially that part of it that involved the emergency core-cooling system, was totally inadequate to deal with the kinds of worst-case accidents that could result in reactor core meltdowns. The news of the Idaho tests caused consternation at the AEC. At the time the tests were completed, fifty-five large nuclear power plants were under construction, some of them all but complete. The tests not only raised embarrassing questions about whether these plants should be licensed; they forced sensible people to question whether any more such plants should even be considered for licensing pending a serious review of plant design and the development and testing of new safety equipment. The AEC handled the test results almost exactly as it had handled the revised version of WASH-740. It made no public announcement, appointed an in-house task force to review the problem, and hoped that what it so desperately wanted to keep confidential would remain that way—at least for a while.[6]

Meanwhile, together with representatives of the nuclear industry, the AEC conducted an exercise in damage control. It set up a task force, none of whose members was an expert in ECCS, to study the problem. The task force met extensively with representatives of the reactor manufacturers, who presented their own data. Rejecting the results of the Idaho tests, the industry people offered computer projections showing that ECCS would work exactly as they should when they were needed. The Idaho engineers countered with a detailed report of their own, which contained, among other conclusions, the considered judgment that reactor cooling problems were so complex and the available data so limited that making an accurate computer model was simply not possible. Therefore, it concluded, the industry's computer model could not be trusted to predict how reactors would perform.

The debate continued through 1971, becoming more arcane and more acrimonious with each round. But it settled nothing.

And word about the substance of the debate did manage to leak out. Ever since Shippingport, a small core of environmentalists, scientists, and informed private citizens had been concerned about whether nuclear power plants posed hazards to the environment, their immediate neighbors, and the general public. Like many within the AEC, these opponents of the atom had found themselves able to accept small, widely scattered nuclear power plants. But during the midsixties, when the AEC and the industry had begun scaling up the sizes of their plants, these groups had begun to get more concerned, both about nuclear development in general and about the AEC and its father-knows-best attitude in particular.

Many of these people thought that they would get a chance to air their doubts or raise questions about reactor safety when the AEC opened formal hearings on the adequacy of its 1971 policy on ECCS in January 1972. They were wrong. The AEC had neither the desire nor the intention to open up the process of decision making on reactor safety to the public. Its hearings were an administrative maneuver designed to limit public questioning on the matter. Those opposed to the licensing of plants like New York's Indian Point 2, Michigan's Midland, and the Pilgrim plant at Plymouth, Massachusetts, had raised the ECCS question at hearings on those installations after they had learned the results of the Idaho tests. Their questions had led lawyers for the utility companies to complain that the ECCS controversy was creating chaos in the reactor licensing process. Their complaint had led to the promulgation of the 1971 AEC policy statement—that current ECCS designs were adequate and that the computer models used by industry to project ECCS performance were sound. The statement meant that, under the AEC's rules, questions about these subjects could no longer be raised in plant-licensing hearings.

The AEC rule did not, however, silence the opponents of individual plants. The commission's regulations notwithstanding, they continued to raise safety questions in hearings. And they began to pick up some support. The original small core of antinuclear activists was swelled during the sixties by a growing number of antiestablishment types—from environmentalists upset at industry and government in general to Vietnam war protesters to scientific and academic groups like the Union of Concerned Scientists. The San Francisco–based Sierra Club, which had gotten into the fight by questioning the siting of a couple of California plants, moved into a position of leadership and began to question nuclear power and policy in general. So did other large environmental groups, like the Natural Resources Defense Council, as well as consumer advocate Ralph Nader, public-interest law firms, and a host of ad hoc groups which, originally organized to oppose specific local plants, eventually banded together into a loose coalition held together by a growing fear of and opposition to the nuclearization of America.

This does not mean that the public opposed nuclear power. As the decade of the seventies got under way, nuclear power enjoyed almost unanimous support in both houses of Congress and strong support among the general public, a large segment of which dismissed the antinuclear movement as a collection of "back-to-nature crazies." But still, the AEC was concerned—and rightly so—by the tactics and growing strength of the antinuclear minority, whose members were increasingly using the federal government's own rules, regulations, and laws to delay plant approvals, slow plant construction, and, in the process, increase the costs of getting a nuclear plant built.

In an attempt to deal with these challenges, the AEC decided not to battle over the issue in each hearing on each nuclear plant license. It decided instead to hold a single "rulemaking" hearing at which, it hoped, it would settle the ECCS controversy once and for all. Other groups welcomed the opportunity. Those who had been

involved in separate hearings agreed to participate in the AEC's unprecedented exercise—the first major public hearing that the agency
had ever held on the question of reactor safety—on the condition
that the AEC allow them to cross-examine the government's expert
witnesses on ECCS. Altogether, some sixty environmental and public-interest groups agreed to take part in the hearing.[7]

The prospect that the hearings might hurt was never far from the
minds of those in charge of organizing them, nor was the possibility
that the hearings might undermine strong, but waning, public support for nuclear power. Both were taken into account as the hearings
and their ground rules were prepared. The AEC's fears were obvious to Daniel Ford, who participated in the hearings on behalf of
the Union of Concerned Scientists. "Containment buildings are intended to limit the accidental escape of radioactive materials from
nuclear plants," wrote Ford in *The Cult of the Atom.* "Similarly, the
ground rules for the hearings were designed to limit the adverse
public-relations fallout from a public discussion of ECCS problems."[8]

The AEC's plan certainly gave it reason for confidence. As the
AEC envisioned things, the hearing would be brief, lasting no more
than six weeks. The AEC would present its scientists, who would
provide some technical backup for the 1971 policy statement. Environmental groups and others critical of the policy statement would
then be allowed to present their arguments. The nuclear power industry would get a chance to put its views on record. The AEC would
then withdraw behind closed doors, consider its action, and, finally,
issue a definitive policy statement to replace and supersede the 1971
statement. This, the AEC figured, would end the controversy and
allow the licensing of nuclear plants to proceed unimpeded.

It sounded neat. The AEC's scientific committee, which had been
purged of its dissenting members, would make no reference to a report critical of the 1971 policy by the ACRS. So the AEC's only other
problem was how to limit what those AEC witnesses who would take
part in the hearing might reveal. The AEC had not been enthusiastic about the idea of allowing its witnesses to be cross-examined. Now,
while it knew that it could control what they said in formal testimony, it was worried about what they might disclose under questioning, especially under questioning by some of the experts the opposition was expected to bring to the hearing.

The AEC handled this dilemma with something less than finesse.
A short time before the hearing opened, the management of the Idaho

test laboratory met with researchers and told them that while they were free to say whatever they pleased during the hearing, it could not assure them that they would still have jobs at the laboratory if what they said failed to please the AEC. The AEC dealt with its in-house staffers by sending each of those scheduled to appear at the hearing a one-page memo titled "Hints at Being a Witness." The memo contained such obvious guidance as urging staffers to dress presentably, to be on time for the proceedings, and to speak up when on the witness stand. But it also instructed witnesses that they were not to volunteer any information that was not directly requested, and it told would-be witnesses quite categorically, despite the fact that they would be testifying under oath, to remember who their employer was. "Never disagree with established policy," said the memo.[9]

The AEC's hearing on ECCS got under way on January 27, 1972. It lasted a good deal longer than the AEC had anticipated. In fact, the hearing lasted two years, and before it ended, in December 1973, it generated more than 50,000 pages of evidence. The hearing also changed the public's perception of nuclear power and the people behind it. Before the hearing began, the vast majority of the public gave little thought to whether it ran any real risks as the result of the operations of a nuclear reactor in the next town or neighboring county. By the time the hearing ended, a substantial minority was convinced that the nuclear plants then being built were inherently unsafe, while even the majority that still liked the idea of nuclear power felt that the plants then being considered could—and should—be made safer.

The hearing began when the members of the AEC task force—minus two dissenting members—took the witness stand and submitted 127 pages of written testimony supporting the AEC's 1971 statement. The testimony was fraught with problems, as the members, who spent the next five weeks defending it, were soon to realize. But then, the agency was fraught with dissent, and it was not long after the hearing opened that some dissenters released a line-by-line critique of the task force report. Nor was it much longer before other dissenters revealed the existence of another in-house report critical of the 1971 decision that the AEC had not planned on releasing. The reports made it clear that the AEC had relied entirely upon the industry it was supposed to regulate for its information on emergency core-cooling systems, and worse, that it had ignored the reservations of some of its best staffers on the question.

The testimony by the task force and its feeble responses to questions that became more pointed as the hearing progressed went a long way toward weakening the AEC's insistence that both it and the industry were doing all they could to protect the public. But the most telling testimony during the hearing came from Philip Rittenhouse, an Oak Ridge metallurgist who had spent most of the past several years trying to determine exactly what would happen to a reactor's uranium fuel rods and the zirconium alloy tubes in which the fuel was packed if a loss-of-coolant accident should occur in a reactor and not be promptly corrected. Rittenhouse had barely begun to testify when he acknowledged that the AEC's analysis of the situation was simply technically incorrect. He also revealed that the task force's calculations had been based not on hard data, but rather on extrapolation and guesswork. Finally, asked if existing reactor design was adequate to prevent an uncovered reactor core from overheating and melting down in the event of a loss-of-coolant accident, Rittenhouse bit the bullet. Knowing that an honest answer would cost him his career with the AEC, he gave it anyway. Existing reactor design, he said forthrightly, was not adequate to prevent a reactor meltdown.[10]

Rittenhouse's testimony, as well as that of other dissenters, including the two who had been removed from the task force prior to the start of the hearings, led to the predictable headlines. *The Washington Post, The New York Times*, the wire services all noted that whatever the feelings of the men at the top levels of the agency, the AEC's scientific experts had their doubts about nuclear reactor safety. The headlines, in turn, led to demands from the antinuclear forces that reactor licensing be suspended pending further hearings on the installation of new safety equipment.

But neither the testimony of its own experts nor the newspaper headlines nor the growing opposition deterred the AEC from reaching the posthearing conclusion that, some of its commissioners made clear, it had intended to reach anyway. In a move that had been telegraphed six months earlier by the AEC's Deputy Director of Licensing, Edson Case, the agency reaffirmed its 1971 statement, claiming, in an exercise truly worthy of *Alice in Wonderland's* Red Queen, that the evidence supported its conclusion. The next few years may have seen a number of changes in AEC personnel as dissenters were demoted, forced out of the agency, or sent to the AEC equivalent of Siberia. But they saw no changes in AEC policy. With the question of emergency core-cooling systems settled to its satisfaction if to no one else's, the AEC went back to business as usual—promoting the expansion of nuclear power, and licensing nuclear plants whose untested ECCS were believed by experts to be inadequate.

The ECCS hearings may not have changed AEC policy, but they did leave the agency with a public relations problem that not even it could ignore. For in the wake of the hearing, the AEC stood revealed as arrogant and insensitive, as being more interested in the needs and concerns of a large, profitable industry than it was in the fears and the concerns, some of them all too justified, of a large and growing segment of the U.S. public.

The ECCS hearings did not change congressional policies toward the AEC, either. A majority of the nation's senators and representatives still felt that nuclear power was both necessary for the U.S. and desirable for its business community and agreed that its development should be promoted. But in Congress, too, the hearing had its effect, particularly on those senators and representatives whose states and districts included large nuclear plants or large antinuclear groups. For, as the congressmen recognized better than the AEC (they were, after all, subject to election and did not hold their jobs by Presidential appointment), no agency of government can long ignore public concerns, and in the increasingly fractious decade of the seventies, no governmental agency—or for that matter, as events would prove, no President—could count on the unquestioning faith of the American people that it knows what was best for everybody.

Glenn Seaborg, who was nothing if not a true believer in the nuclear future, may have believed that he knew what was best for America and Americans. For a few years, at least, most Americans either supported or at least did not question his belief. But James Schlesinger, who replaced Seaborg as head of the AEC in 1971, after the latter had held the job for ten years, far longer than anyone else, recognized the problem. No brighter, but in many ways far more perceptive than Seaborg, Schlesinger needed only look around him to realize that the environmental movement, which was spearheading the attack on the AEC, was picking up followers and public support. Nor did he have to look much farther than his new office to realize that Shakespeare's Cassius was correct when he told Brutus that "the fault is not in our stars, but in ourselves." The AEC, he acknowledged, had failed to calm the controversy over nuclear safety. And, Schlesinger observed, it had failed because it refused to recognize that the controversy was not, as it imagined, a public relations problem. The problem had nothing to do with the AEC's image. What was at issue, Schlesinger conceded, was the agency's policy.[11]

That the AEC was no longer considered infallible was evident in the attitudes of both Congress and the public. It became more evident early in 1979 when the U.S. Court of Appeals for the District of Columbia ruled against the agency in a licensing case. Accepting the argument of the agency's opponents, the court ruled that the AEC was in violation of the National Environmental Policy Act of 1969 for failing, in its licensing procedures, to give proper regard to the environmental impact of proposed nuclear power plants. To get on the right side of the law, the court held, the AEC would henceforth have to prepare detailed environmental impact statements on each plant and to consider their adverse environmental effects before making any licensing decisions. The AEC, the court noted, had been given broad discretionary powers to license nuclear plants. It had not, the court made clear, used these powers well.

Congress, the courts, and the public were not, though, the only sections of U.S. society to turn against nuclear power in the early seventies. The press also joined the pack. For the twenty years since nuclear power's birth, the press had been more claqueur than critic, hailing the industry's accomplishments and progress and downplaying or dismissing nuclear power's opponents as a small band who seemed unable to see the difference between a Hiroshima bomb and a peaceful power plant. But now the press, too, had changed its tune. Like sharks smelling blood, many newspapers and journalists sensed that the industry, once regarded as invulnerable, was ailing. Some, especially those that followed the ECCS hearings, saw the evidence of dissension within the AEC as an indication that the agency had betrayed the public. Some, noting the close relations that prevailed between the AEC and the industry, thought they scented scandal and the smell of corruption. All now regarded the AEC, once considered the vanguard of the scientific forces that would save America, as an agency whose actions must henceforth be watched carefully and reported critically. The JCAE and the power companies may still have had warm thoughts for the AEC, but, as the seventies got under way, it became increasingly clear that, outside its small circle, the AEC had few friends.

Schlesinger was quick to appreciate the AEC's changed position. He realized that the agency needed a new, improved image. But he was astute enough to realize that a new image alone would not solve the agency's problems. The agency, Schlesinger conceded, would have to change some of its policies as well.

The first of those, Schlesinger announced, would be to accept the decision of the court of appeals and to prepare environmental impact statements as required before making any decisions on the licensing of nuclear plants. The second, revealed at a meeting with the nuclear power industry, was to admit error and to concede that, for a regulator, the AEC had developed an unhealthy relationship with the industry it regulated. The third was to concede that those opposed to nuclear power were something other than "ecofreaks," and to admit that the environmentalists had raised many pertinent questions about nuclear development and safety and to pledge that in the years to come the AEC would respond to these questions as a "referee" serving the public rather than as a spokesman for the nuclear power industry. The industry, he said, would have to accept the AEC's new role. It would also do well to acknowledge that it had not done all it possibly could do to guarantee that nuclear plants were safe or to make sure that work done on these plants met the high standards that the public had a right to expect.

Believing, with the Bible, that confession is good for the soul, the press responded favorably to Schlesinger's public act of contrition, hailing what it took, at face value, to be his good intentions. Industry, though with less enthusiasm, took a similar position. Instead of arguing with the new AEC chairman, it voiced public agreement with his ideas. But both also remained skeptical. The industry wondered if Schlesinger actually meant to act on his ideas, and so did the press, which increasingly found that stories on poorly constructed, unsafe nuclear power plants made good copy.

Their skepticism was well-founded. The industry need not have worried. It quickly became clear that Schlesinger, despite his orders to the AEC to prepare voluminous environmental impact statements, intended no real changes in the way the agency operated. For, as the chairman himself declared, the safety issue was settled. Schlesinger conceded that nuclear accidents, including the "worst case" mishaps in which everything that could possibly go wrong actually did, were within the realm of at least theoretical possibility. But the probability that such an accident would occur, he insisted, was remote. There were so many safety devices in use, so many safety precautions taken at every nuclear plant that the risks of such an accident actually occurring were infinitesimal. One stood a greater chance of being struck by a meteorite, he said, than one did of dying as a result of a nuclear plant accident.

The AEC's assurances did little to mollify the agency's critics, who wanted more specific information. They did not want to be assured that the chances of an accident were small; they wanted to know what those chances actually were. And the AEC was unable to tell them. Pressed to provide information on the actual likelihood of a loss-of-coolant accident, the AEC was not able to come up with any believable numbers. Seeking to do so, the agency classified accidents into nine groups, ranging from Class 1 mishaps involving minor malfunctions of equipment at nuclear plants to Class 9 catastrophes. The agency said that there would be no environmental impact from accidents up to Class 8, which involved major disruptions of the plant that would necessitate the operation of the plant's emergency safety systems. Only Class 9 accidents would affect the environment, and they were not covered in the environmental impact statements. Why? Because the probabilities of such accidents could not be calculated, conceded an AEC scientist.[12]

The AEC's quandary is understandable. The probability of many events can be fairly easily calculated. One need not have a degree in statistics to figure out the chances of drawing a particular card from a deck, or even be a particularly good poker player to figure the odds against drawing a straight flush at the green-covered table. Nor need one find it all that difficult to calculate such things as the likelihood that an automobile driver of a particular age or sex will smash his car into another. There is a large statistical base, accumulated by insurance companies over years of doing business, from which such a calculation might not only be made, but made with some degree of accuracy.

But calculating the risks of a major accident is much more difficult. A nuclear power plant is not a simple thing like a coin, which has only two sides. It is not even as simple as an automobile or an airplane, each of which has tens or dozens or even hundreds of moving parts. A nuclear power plant is a machine of consummate complexity, a maze of pipes, valves, wires, relays, and mechanical linkages, any one of which can malfunction. Calculating the possibility and the probability that a given valve might malfunction is within the ability of most engineers and mathematicians. But a major accident in a nuclear plant involves more than the failure of a single, probably redundant part. It involves the failure of a great many components, which must not only break down but do so in a certain order and in certain combinations with others in order to lead to the kind of accident that would result in the overheating of the core, the breach of the reactor's containment building, and the release of radioactive materials into the atmosphere.

The beginning of the year 1972 found the AEC unable to provide the public with a realistic assessment of the chances that a serious nuclear accident might occur. But the year opened with the AEC convinced of the need to assemble such information, and imbued with the willingness to try. Prodded by Schlesinger, the AEC began to plan a serious study of accident probabilities.

In making these plans, however, the AEC did not turn to recognized experts in the fields of statistics or authorities on probability theory. Instead of going outside, the agency decided to conduct its study using its own people and resources. The reason for its decision was obvious: the AEC wanted to maintain complete control over both the study and such parts of it as it might choose to release.

At the same time, though, the AEC did not want its actions to be obvious. For the sake of credibility, it wanted the study at least to seem to be an independent undertaking. To create this appearance, it sought to recruit an outsider to serve as the project's titular director. The outsider it chose was Dr. Manson Benedict, who headed the nuclear engineering department at the Massachusetts Institute of Technology; he was a long-time proponent of nuclear power who had once served as a member of the Atomic Industrial Forum's board of directors. But Benedict, to the AEC's disappointment, declined the honor of being in full charge of the project. He did, however, offer the agency another name. He suggested that the AEC give the post to Dr. Norman Rasmussen, another member of MIT's nuclear engineering faculty. Rasmussen's credentials were impeccable. He had worked as a consultant to several nuclear industry groups and was a founding member of Americans for Energy Independence, a Westinghouse-financed group that lobbied strongly for nuclear power. A native of Pennsylvania (he grew up on a farm only a few miles from Three Mile Island), Rasmussen admitted that he had no background in statistics or any of the other areas necessary to oversee the study about to be launched. Nor had he written extensively about nuclear power. He had, in fact, published just a single, totally nontechnical article in which he had argued, based on data supplied by industry sources, that existing ECCS were adequate to prevent nuclear power plants from melting down.[13]

Appointed to head the project, Rasmussen, aided by Benedict, lost little time preparing a study outline in which it was suggested that the project be guided by a steering committee that would include MIT faculty members as well as representatives of the reactor manufacturers. The outline also acknowledged that the AEC would have the final say on how the study's results would be made public.

Almost from the start, the study came under criticism. Many critics found fault with the fact that the study group did not do a general survey of all the nuclear plants in the U.S. Instead, it looked at a pair of representative plants that used the two most common types of nuclear reactors. The Surry Nuclear Power Station Unit 1 in Surry County, Virginia, used a pressurized water reactor manufactured by Westinghouse. The Peach Bottom Nuclear Power Station in York County, Pennsylvania, had a boiling water reactor built by General Electric. The study did not really look all that closely at either. Though the reactor-safety study staff did make several visits to each plant, it obtained most of its information from the two companies that built the facilities, and relied on industry sources for much of the actual analysis that went into the study.

This, however, was not the only criticism of the study. Even more critics objected to the analytical methods used.

Their objections were understandable. The major method used was something called "fault-tree analysis," a method in which engineers analyze a particular system, look at the individual "faults," such as human error, mechanical breakdowns, and natural factors, that are possible, and then draw diagrams that attempt to show how small independent faults might combine to produce certain "sequences" that could lead to a serious accident. Once this is done, the engineers take data on the probability of each individual accident occurring and then use the information to compute the likelihood that a particular set of accidents could occur, in a particular order, to disrupt the system.

The problem, the critics compalined, is that fault-tree analysis has its limitations and that these limitations are severe. Fault-tree analysis works well with fairly simple systems; it tends to break down when confronted by exceedingly complex systems for the simple reason that no one can be sure that all possible occurrences have been factored into its equations. Engineers working on the National Aeronautics and Space Administration's Apollo Program knew of these shortcomings only too well. Some 20 percent of the ground-test failures in the program, and more than 35 percent of all in-flight malfunctions involved failures that had not been previously identified as realistic possibilities.

Critics argued that a fault-tree analysis of potential nuclear accidents would be equally flawed. Risks to the public, they said, could not be determined merely by studying the machinery of a nuclear plant. Other things had to be considered as well, such as the strength and direction of the prevailing winds, or the question of whether people in the area could be evacuated in time to avoid injury in the event of an accident.

Despite these criticisms, though, the study went ahead. Benedict and Rasmussen had originally expected that the study could be completed in eleven months. They were wrong. A full year after it began, the study was still far from complete; indeed, the researchers seemed to have even more questions after a year's work than they had when they started. Some of the questions concerned policy. The members of the study group knew what the AEC's policy was on nuclear reactors. They worried that their findings might not support such a policy, or worse, that they might call it into question. They were also concerned with the implications of their looking too closely at the construction and operation of the two representative plants. Schlesinger had already given the industry a mild reproof, noting that it was frequently guilty of not merely tolerating but of actually encouraging shoddy workmanship. The members of the study group were afraid that their examination of the Surry and Peach Bottom plants might reveal such workmanship. They knew that their study and its findings should strengthen public confidence in nuclear power and the way in which it was being managed. What they feared was that the report might have the opposite effect.

Their fears were not unfounded. The working draft, completed in the summer of 1974, covered three thousand pages and was, in its printed form, thicker than a Manhattan telephone directory. It was also released hurriedly. Though the study had taken two years to complete, a review panel was given just ten days to examine it and to note any omissions, errors, and inconsistencies.

That the time was insufficient was obvious. Some reviewers did not even attempt to go over the voluminous report. But Dr. Daniel Kleitman did. Using his time to best advantage, he reviewed the statistical methods used in preparing the report and found them wanting. The study, he concluded, was heavily biased toward optimistic estimates of accident probability. The probabilities would have been higher by a factor of two or more if better statistical methods had been used. Along with other reviewers, he urged that the study be held and substantially redone, this time with less bias.[14]

His appeal was ignored. The AEC had already set August 20 as the date for releasing the study, which it considered the first salvo in what it hoped would be a final and successful battle against the forces opposed to nuclear power. And the agency was already touting the study's results, hinting to reporters that they showed nuclear accidents to be so unlikely as to be virtually impossible. Dixy Lee Ray, who became the AEC's chairman after Schlesinger left to head the Central Intelligence Agency, told all who would listen that the study showed the probability of a reactor accident leading to a meltdown to be only one in a million.[15]

But Ray, too, was wrong. When, following the release of several unofficial estimates, the actual figures were released, they showed the probabilities of a meltdown to be much greater. The Reactor Safety Study of 1975, released as WASH-1400, and known since then as the Rasmussen Report, concluded that a reactor core meltdown and a breach of nuclear plant containment could be expected to take place once in every 20,000 years of reactor operation, or once every 200 years for a country with one hundred operating nuclear power plants. It concluded that there would be one chance in 10,000 that the weather, the distribution of the population, and the seriousness of the radiation release would combine to produce what the study group considered the "worst case" scenario.

The scenario was a bad one, its consequences dire. According to the study, such a worst-case accident would cause 3,300 prompt fatalities from burns and acute radiation sickness and afflict another 45,000 with less acute burns and injuries. Its long-term consequences would be equally disastrous. The study concluded that such an accident would cause 240,000 cases of thyroid disease over a period of 30 years and some 30,000 cases of genetic disorders, some fatal, over a period of 150 years. Most dramatic, such an accident would cause 45,000 cancer fatalities, most of them resulting from exposure suffered during the first week of fallout from the mishap.

Nor would these be the accident's only effects. Such an accident, the experts estimated, would contaminate 3,200 square miles of land. The economic loss resulting from this contamination would be a staggering $14 billion.[16]

The AEC hailed the study as a vindication of its policies, calling the risks outlined in the report's conclusions acceptable. Treating WASH-1400 as an independent effort by MIT rather than a carefully managed in-house operation, the agency did not mention the comments of its own internal review group or the fact that the group's two hundred pages of comments were not being made public.

The press joined in the laudatory comments, echoing the AEC line that the study reaffirmed what the agency had been saying all along about reactor safety and speculating that the antinuclear forces had been dealt a death blow. Only the scientific community failed to join in the general atmosphere of approval. The *Bulletin of the Atomic Scientists* noted that the report was not an independent evaluation of the AEC's performance or policies on nuclear reactor safety, merely "a defense of them." [17]

Others continued to find fault with the study's statistical methods. Given the fact that operators, builders, and regulators had all had relatively little experience with plant failures, many felt that it was impossible to make anything even approaching an accurate evaluation of the probabilities of most single events, let alone multiple events happening in a nuclear plant. Thus, responsible critics concluded, the Rasmussen Report's estimates of accident probabilities could have been high or low by a factor of as much as 500; the science involved was that inexact.

The criticism was timely—and on target. A number of people, especially in Congress and the various consumer groups that attempted to influence it, had been arguing for some time that the AEC needed to be reorganized. There was, they said, no real way to resolve the conflict between the AEC's two mandated roles. It was simply not possible to combine the functions of regulator and promoter within the same agency. Licensing nuclear power stations and supervising their operations requires a conservative approach that puts safety before all other considerations. Such an approach cannot be reconciled with a promotional zeal to see the industry grow and expand.

The result of such a realization was the Energy Reorganization Act of 1974. Under this piece of legislation, the AEC's nonregulatory functions—including those of weapons design and manufacture, reactor design, and the production of nuclear materials—were split off from the agency's regulatory functions. The nonregulatory part of the AEC's job description was taken over by a new body called the Energy Research and Development Administration (ERDA). The regulatory part of the job was given to an independent agency called the Nuclear Regulatory Commission (NRC). ERDA was placed under the aegis of a single administrator appointed by the President.

The NRC was placed under the command of five appointed commissioners.[18]

Creating an independent regulatory body to license and supervise nuclear power plants and the development of the industry was viewed as a constructive step. But not as a final solution to the problem of nuclear plant safety. For there is still considerable doubt even today as to whether the NRC has wholly abandoned the old AEC role of promoting the industry. The Kemeny Commission, appointed by President Carter to study the 1979 accident at Three Mile Island, found the NRC "so preoccupied with the licensing of plants that it has not given primary consideration to overall safety issues."[19]

The commission's finding came as no surprise to anyone. The AEC was told early in its existence that it could choose between safety or development of the industry. Speaking to the agency's Advisory Committee on Reactor Safeguards late in 1953, no less an authority than Edward Teller, father of the H-bomb, conceded that if the U.S. built nuclear power plants, then accidents were bound to occur. A short time later, Teller was even more specific, noting that "no legislation will be able to stop future accidents and avoid completely occasional loss of life." Nuclear plants, he made clear, could not be separated from the dangers they posed. But, Teller urged, the AEC should take these dangers in stride and, while taking steps to promote and improve safety, not let fear of accidents prevent it from playing the role of promoter in addition to that of regulator. Said Teller: "[T]he unavoidable danger which will remain after all reasonable controls have been employed must not stand in the way of rapid development of nuclear power."[20]

The AEC and its successor, the NRC, both heeded Teller's advice. Unfortunately for both, their decision cost them a good part of their credibility. Nor, in the long run, did it help the industry. Like a precocious child indulged by its parents and doted on by its teachers, the nuclear power industry grew too fast, running before it was able to walk, and leaping in less than twenty years from a fledgling industry with a few small, manageable plants to a multibillion-dollar industry apparently convinced that only big could be beautiful. Growing more slowly might have helped the industry to develop more carefully, to work out the bugs in its small- and medium-sized plants before going on to build bigger ones. But growing uncontrolled, like a cancer, proved to be ultimately unhealthy for the industry. Critics looking at the nuclear power industry in the early seventies found it an economic and technological mess, and wondered how much longer it would be able to survive without either a bankruptcy or a major accident—or both.

They did not have to wonder very long. The decade of the seventies provided the answer to one part of their question. The decade of the eighties would provide the answer to the other.

Five

No Business Like Nuke Business

"When I was seventeen," begins the ballad popularized by Frank Sinatra, "it was a very good year." And not the only such year. The song goes on to describe other good years: "When I was twenty-one . . . when I was thirty-five . . ." Like the singer, the nuclear power industry had its good years, too. In fact, during the late sixties and midseventies, it had several of them, fat years in the biblical sense, years during which it seemed that everything was going its way and that the future that nuclear enthusiasts had been predicting for years had finally arrived.

There were several reasons why the end of the sixties and the beginning of the seventies looked so good for nuclear power and its proponents. One, of course, was the support the industry received from the government, which not only promoted nuclear power but also turned a blind eye toward some of its most obvious and pressing problems. The nuclear power industry, it was evident, had friends in high places, friends who very much wanted it to succeed.

Another was the growing realization that the age of abundant, inexpensive oil was drawing to a close. The fifties and sixties had seen the discovery of huge reserves of oil in the Middle East, in the West African nation of Nigeria, in South America. Eager to sell the oil that was making them wealthy, these oil-rich nations pumped it out of their desert or jungle soil and shipped it at low cost to Europe, the U.S., and Japan.

Taking advantage of oil's abundance, the international oil companies kept its price artificially low and sold it cheap, persuading many utilities to build large oil-fired power plants and ousting coal as the dominant fuel powering industry and generating electricity. Suddenly, coal seemed too dirty and old-fashioned for industry to use, a throwback to the age of the Industrial Revolution. Many companies converted their coal-burning plants to oil burners. Though the U.S. was partially insulated from the oil takeover by import restrictions reserving 88 percent of the world's largest market for domestic production, utilities in other countries ordered oil-fired plants under the impression that they would be saving money on fuel. In a few countries, like Germany and Great Britain, pressure from coal companies and mine workers' unions slowed down the rate at which oil infiltrated the field of electric generation. In France and Japan, oil's victory was unconditional.[1]

A third reason for the nuclear industry's unqualified optimism was the rate at which the U.S. economy—and the concomitant demand for energy—was growing. In the ten years between 1963 and 1973, the demand for electricity grew at an average rate of 7.3 percent a year.[2] American industry was expanding, using more and more power. American consumers were also increasing their use of electricity. Heeding the slogan "Better living through electricity," and hypnotized by the siren song being sung by companies like Westinghouse and General Electric, Americans owned more electrical appliances and consumed more electricity than anyone else in the world. Americans were, in fact, the world's most profligate users of energy. Americans used millions of kilowatts of electricity to light their homes, to wash their clothes, to run their television sets, and to chill the beer they drank as they sat and watched programs on those television sets. There seemed, at least as far as the people in the utility industry could see, no reason why they should not keep doing so forever.

But in fact, there were several reasons. One was that the price of oil was creeping slowly upward. Realizing the political power their oil reserves gave them, the nations that made up the membership of the Organization of Petroleum Exporting Countries (OPEC) had been pushing the prices of Middle Eastern, Nigerian, and South American crude slowly upward, moving it from a low of $5.40 a barrel in 1965 to more than $10 a barrel by the end of the decade.[3]

These increases were, of course, felt both at the gas pump and in the prices charged for power by oil-burning utilities, which passed their increased costs promptly along to their customers. Consumers spent the late sixties and the first years of the seventies watching their electric bills increase by an average of 2 percent a year, and complaining, though not too loudly, as the price of gasoline crept upward by a penny here, two cents there.

At first no one seemed particularly concerned. The price hikes were absorbed, if not with ease, then at least without undue difficulty. Only a few industry types heeded the handwriting that was beginning to appear, albeit faintly, on the wall. "Oil prices are increasing," said the writing. "Oil prices will continue to increase."

In anticipation of such increases, many oil companies began turning, especially in the late sixties, to nuclear power, seeing the atom as the answer to their energy questions and envisioning uranium as the fuel that would prove cheapest in the long run. Between 1970 and 1973, as oil prices doubled, orders for nuclear capacity tripled, rising from 20,000 to a staggering 60,000 megawatts.[4]

One of the biggest buyers of nuclear capacity was Japan. The Japanese had good reason for going nuclear. In fact, they had several. One was that the country had experienced twenty years of double-digit growth. In the early 1950s, the Japanese economy was only one-third the size of that of either Britain or France. By the late 1970s, it was bigger than both combined. Japan's gross national product had surpassed that of Britain in 1962, that of France in 1963, that of Germany in 1966. By the midseventies, Japan's industrial output had exceeded that of the U.S.S.R. and ranked second only to that of the U.S. Demand for electricity had risen with the country's gross national product, and this demand made it essential for the Japanese to look toward nuclear power as a way to meet it. Japan had few alternatives; 85 percent of the country's energy came from abroad.[5]

Demand, though, was not the only factor that tempted the Japanese to look toward nuclear power as a source of energy. The country's rapid industrialization and its tremendous population growth had given it the worst urban congestion and some of the most serious pollution problems of any advanced nation. Coal-fired plants, the Japanese realized, would only exacerbate these problems. But nuclear power, which Japanese technocrats saw as "clean," would, if not help solve the problems, then at least not make them worse.

In the U.S. the government fostered the growth of nuclear power. In Japan the nuclearization of the country was carried out by two

private firms whose rivalry served to accelerate the process. Kikawada Kazutaka, president of Tokyo Electric, the world's largest privately owned utility, and Ashihara Yoshishige, president of Kansai
Electric Company, shared a typically Japanese belief that big business should display greater social responsibility and a less typical
feeling that nuclear power was the best thing for their country. Though
they were strong corporate rivals, the two men also shared a deep
belief that business, particularly the business of generating electric
power, should remain in private hands; they wanted nothing like the
TVA in their country. The two men had begun battling public power
back in 1939 when the country's military government had created a
single nationalized utility and organized the country's power system
into nine regional "companies." In the years following the war, the
two power-company presidents managed to convince American oc-
cupation authorities to keep the nine companies but to abandon the
idea of a centralized system except in one area. Because none of the
companies commanded the capital to finance plant construction, the
task of building new facilities was to remain in public hands. Appalled, the directors of the companies countered by proposing a consortium, which the Americans accepted. The result was the Japanese Atomic Power Company (JAPCO), which in 1957 bought Japan's
first nuclear reactor—a gas-cooled model from Great Britain.[6]

Unfortunately for the British, Japan's experience with their reactor was unsatisfactory. So, early in the sixties, the Japanese put
out the word that they were interested in other designs. General
Electric and Westinghouse were both interested in making sales. The
two companies pitched their products intensively. But GE won the
sales race, and in 1965 JAPCO ordered a plant similar to the company's Oyster Creek model. Within a year, Tokyo Electric and Kansai both decided to buy their own plants. Their purchases had little
to do with the technical qualities of the rival plants. Like most Japanese companies, both Tokyo and Kansai were tied by tradition to
certain suppliers, preferring established relationships to the open-
ended practice of dealing with bids. Tokyo had always bought its plants
from GE; Kansai had always purchased its equipment from Westinghouse. They followed this tradition when it came to buying nuclear
plants. In 1966 Kansai ordered a pressurized water reactor from
Westinghouse. Tokyo followed Kansai's order with one of its own and
bought a boiling water reactor from GE. In so doing, they started
Japan down a road that seemed to lead in one direction only—toward nuclear power.[7]

Japan, the only country to suffer a nuclear bombing, welcomed nuclear power enthusiastically, so enthusiastically, in fact, that the Japanese Atomic Energy Commission quickly revised its view of the country's nuclear future. In 1961 the commission had estimated that Japan would have 6,000 to 8,000 megawatts of nuclear capacity on-line by 1985. In 1967 the commission upped its estimate by a factor of five and predicted that the country would have 30,000 to 40,000 megawatts of capacity installed by the mideighties. In 1970 it revised its figures again and predicted 60,000 megawatts.[8]

Japan, though, was not the only country to fall in love with the atom during this period. France's state-owned utility, Électricité de France (EDF), had given the country two decades of low rates and good management, as well as leadership for the nation's efforts to rebuild its war-ravaged economy. In 1971, flushed with success, EDF launched a program to sell even more electricity and to provide it by means of nuclear power. *"Toute électrique! Toute nucléaire!* (All electric! All nuclear!)" became the slogan of the EDF campaign to improve the quality of life in France. Never mind that all EDF really wanted to do was sell more appliances. Like others, it felt that it could accomplish this by offering abundant power and by presenting electricity, particularly that generated by splitting atoms, as cleaner and more modern than that operated by either coal or oil.[9]

EDF had not always been an advocate of nuclear power. In fact, during the sixties, it had resisted pressure from the French atomic energy commission, the Commissariat à L'Énergie Atomique (CEA). Nor had it shown any enthusiasm for the indigenous French technology of gas-graphite reactors. As late as 1970, convinced that oil would remain abundant, EDF had been content to experiment cautiously with American-designed light-water reactors without making any major purchases. It was only when the first round of oil price hikes began that EDF really decided to go nuclear.

But at the beginning, the EDF campaign relied more on public relations than plant construction. Between 1971 and 1973, EDF ordered only a modest 3,000 to 4,000 megawatts of nuclear capacity a year, more as insurance against the growing uncertainties of oil supplies than as a major commitment to the atom. But in the aftermath of the 1973 Yom Kippur War, EDF suddenly scrapped its go-slow approach. Under prodding from the government, EDF ordered 13,000 megawatts of capacity for 1976 and took out options to buy another 11,000. Like the Japanese, EDF committed itself totally. The year 1976 saw France with only ten small reactors producing less than

3,000 megawatts. Under its new plan, the country was committed to thirty new plants producing nearly 30,000 megawatts by the end of 1984.[10]

The French did not, however, care to purchase their nuclear plants from abroad, especially if that meant buying them from either the U.S. or Britain. Instead, the country hoped to use its decision to go nuclear as a springboard to developing its own industry. EDF was delighted with the idea. Even more delighted was Michel Hug, who headed EDF's Direction de l'Équipement, the department responsible for planning and building power plants. Hug had long been a passionate promoter of nuclear power.

French opposition to buying American was not unusual. The almost universal use of U.S.-designed light-water reactors had long been viewed as a challenge by the nuclear engineers of Britain, France, and Germany, who were eager to develop their own. Especially annoying to Europeans was the U.S. monopoly of the supply of enriched uranium, which the American weapons program gave the U.S. the means to produce. The British and French refusal to buy light-water reactors, therefore, was due only in part to patriotism. It was also a result of their fears of becoming dependent upon the U.S. for nuclear fuel. The U.S. already dominated the $50 billion nuclear power business. Europeans, who had the technological and financial means to develop their own industries, were determined that this domination not be allowed to become complete. Convinced that both they and their neighbors must go nuclear, European countries saw no reason why they should not compete with the U.S. in reactor design and construction and grab themselves a share of what all were convinced would be a rapidly expanding market.[11]

The French were particularly avid for a piece of the nuclear action. André Giraud, who became head of the CEA in 1970, envisioned a plan under which France would challenge U.S. dominance in both reactors and fuel. Indeed, he envisioned the creation of a multinational corporation that would do in the nuclear field what oil companies did in petroleum, from mining the uranium ore to designing and building the reactors that would use it to generate electric power.

Giraud's plan may have been grandiose, but Giraud himself was realistic. He knew that France could not quickly produce a reactor capable of competing with the American light-water machines. So he concentrated on mastering what was known as the "nuclear fuel cycle," the processing and handling of uranium through all its var-

ious stages, from mining through enrichment of the ore to the manufacture of fuel rods to the extraction of plutonium from the spent
fuel rods and the reprocessing of the "burned up" uranium into new
fuel elements.

His plan made sense. The French already had a small enrichment plant in which they had produced the materials for their nuclear weapons. Britain also had fuel-processing capability. Several U.S.
energy companies, notably Exxon, Gulf, GE, and Westinghouse,
taking advantage of laws allowing the private ownership of nuclear
materials, were developing it. Germany, which lacked a weapons
program, was also interested in reprocessing.

But no one was more determined to break the U.S. uranium monopoly than Giraud. Developing mines in France and in the former
French colonies of Gabon and Niger, Giraud began to stockpile uranium for use in the CEA's gas-graphite reactor program. Other nations also worked hard at developing their resources. Mines in Canada, South Africa, and the Belgian Congo began producing large
quantities of uranium. The result of their production was a uranium
glut—and falling uranium prices. In 1967 the AEC had declared that
it would sell enriched uranium to anyone at $6 a pound. In 1971, as
the glut continued, uranium prices outside the U.S. dropped to $4.50
a pound, or less than the cost of production for most mines.[12]

To deal with the problems caused by the glut, the French called
a meeting of the non-American fuel-processing nations—France,
Canada, South Africa, Britain, and eventually Austria. This group,
which came to be known as the "Club of Five," divided up the world
uranium market, exclusive of the U.S., between them, setting a
minimum price of $6.25 a pound for the enriched ore. Assuming that
this solved at least part of his problem, Giraud then attempted to
corner the European market for reprocessed fuel, and invested a
fortune in a state-of-the-art gas-diffusion plant to handle the task. The
plant was nothing if not ambitious. Powered by four 900-megawatt
reactors to be built by EDF, it was to produce enough fuel to power
one hundred reactors that size. But the investment proved unwise.
Already, by the midseventies, countries were beginning to reconsi-
der the wisdom of their sudden plunge into nuclear power. Orders
for new nuclear plants were fewer and farther between. Cancellations were becoming common. As a result, the world found itself faced
with more enrichment capacity than it needed or seemed likely to
need. The French in particular found themselves stuck with expensive gas-diffusion technology and no market for their product. A wiser,

more cautious man might have slowed down or at least paused to take stock of his position. Giraud did neither. With an intellectual rigidity that most non-French could not fathom, he continued to invest French funds in what critics, remembering the economic disaster that resulted when their country let nationalistic pride get it involved in the program to build a supersonic transport plane, called "another Concorde." The critics were right. Giraud's ambition brought France no wealth. Instead, it brought it to the brink of economic disaster.

France's failure to break the U.S. nuclear monopoly was ironic. The French certainly tried hard enough. But, as it turned out, it was Germany, the country in which the fission of uranium had first been theorized in 1938, that succeeded.[13]

Germany got into the nuclear business at what must be considered a bargain-basement rate. The huge engineering firm of Siemens AG paid Westinghouse a royalty of $2 million for the right to use its design for a pressurized water reactor. Then, investing $50 million of its own money, the company joined forces with AEG-Telefunken, which was licensed to build GE-designed boiling water reactors. Together Siemens and Telefunken formed the only nuclear manufacturing group capable of competing seriously with the U.S. builders. By 1975 the new group had scored significantly in the international marketplace by winning a Brazilian order for eight reactors. The following year, it sold two reactors to Iran.

This does not mean that the Germans were America's only competitor in the international arena. By the middle of the decade, Canada had sold half a dozen of its own CANDU reactors, a heavy-water machine, to overseas customers; the Swedes had sold a pair of their home-designed pressurized water reactors to neighboring Finland.[14]

Meanwhile, the Soviet Union was also getting into the nuclear power business. Spearheaded by research carried out at Moscow's prestigious Kurchatov Institute, the Soviet nuclearization drive succeeded, by the midseventies, in getting some two dozen reactors online, including two within the city limits of Moscow. The Soviet drive was, of course, unhampered by opposition from environmentalists and antinuclear forces. "We have no Jane Fonda here," a Soviet nuclear engineer boasted when he guided a delegation of American journalists through the huge reactor complex at Novovoronezh in 1978.

An ambitious program, the U.S.S.R's plunge into nuclear power aimed to take advantage of Soviet uranium resources, which were large, and to reduce the country's use of oil, which it preferred to sell abroad for badly needed hard cash. The Soviets also worked at selling reactors abroad, particularly to Warsaw Pact countries, which could not afford to buy U.S.- or European-made machines. During the seventies, the Soviets sold pressurized water reactors of their own design and manufacture to Bulgaria, Hungary, Czechoslovakia, and East Germany. They also managed to sell one to Finland.

In an arrangement that seemed satisfactory to both parties, the Soviets built a 420-megawatt pressurized water reactor for Finland's Imatran Voima Oy at Loviisa, a small town in the south of the country on the Gulf of Finland. Under the terms of the arrangement, the Soviets agreed to supply the Finns with the fuel for their plant, which is fitted with German-made instruments. The Finns, for their part, agreed to send their spent fuel rods back to the U.S.S.R. for reprocessing.

Hailed by the Soviet Union as an example of its entry into the international nuclear market, the Loviisa plant is impressive. But the Soviet sales program is not. Finland, which has a long, indefensible border with the U.S.S.R. and which maintains a special relationship with its large, greedy neighbor to the east, is the only Western nation to purchase a Soviet-made nuclear power plant.[15]

But not even the burgeoning Soviet nuclear program could seriously threaten U.S. nuclear hegemony. The early seventies found U.S. reactor manufacturers riding a wave of prosperity. Business was good. Orders for reactors were pouring in to both GE and Westinghouse, and flowing in to the offices of Babcock and Wilcox and Combustion Engineering in sufficient numbers to make those firms optimistic about the future. Demand for power was rising steadily. Utilities were not merely building nuclear plants; they were also ordering coal- and oil-fired facilities.

But then the bubble burst. It burst in 1973 when, in the wake of the Yom Kippur War, which attempted—and failed—to destroy the state of Israel, members of OPEC raised the price of oil from around $2.50 to $11 per barrel. It burst when a number of OPEC nations imposed an embargo and actually cut off oil shipments to the U.S. as well as to certain other nations whose policies toward Israel they found unacceptable. The embargo hit the U.S. harder than it had to. The U.S. actually imported less than 10 percent of its oil from the Arab nations. But several European nations and Japan received almost all their oil from these countries, and the U.S. had obligated itself to assure their supplies, even if it meant selling them some of our own oil.

The embargo sent the price of oil and oil products skyrocketing. Long lines formed at U.S. gas stations, and fights broke out as Americans, accustomed to abundant supplies of fuel for their cars, bridled at the idea of lining up to fill their tanks and objected to the odd-even systems of rationing imposed in several states. Utility company executives talked darkly of substantially increased gas and electric bills.

The embargo hit the U.S. hard, serving as a warning that the country had become dangerously dependent upon outsiders for its energy sources and reminding Americans that the fuel they took so much for granted could not, even under the best of circumstances, be expected to last forever.[16]

The U.S., typically, sought a quick fix for its problem. President Richard Nixon and members of his administration offered one. Viewing nuclear power, in which the U.S. was world leader, as the way of reducing America's need for foreign oil and freeing it from the risk of what he termed "energy blackmail," the President launched "Project Independence," a program that aimed at nothing less than having the U.S. get half its electricity from nuclear power by the year 2000.[17]

The President's plan seemed sound at the time. Demand for electricity in the U.S. had been rising steadily for the past decade. In some parts of the Sunbelt, the fast-growing area of the U.S. South and Southwest, in fact, demand for electricity was doubling every seven years, or practically overnight for the utility industry, which normally makes its plans on a fifteen-to-twenty-year schedule.

But the demand was not about to continue. The first "oil shock" stunned Americans and made them think less about getting more energy than about using less. For the first time in their lives, Americans began to conserve fuel and energy. Many confined their efforts to nothing more than shutting off unused lights. But many went much further. Realizing that maintaining their present level of energy usage was going to prove expensive—assuming that it even proved possible—large numbers of Americans went on saving sprees. Many realized that they could cut their energy bills by keeping their homes a bit cooler and save on gasoline by driving less. Others studied their patterns of energy usage and began to make their homes and businesses more energy-efficient, installing insulation to cut their heating bills in winter, relying less on power-guzzling air conditioners in the summer. Some began to buy newly marketed energy-efficient appliances. Many questioned whether they really needed such appliances at all.

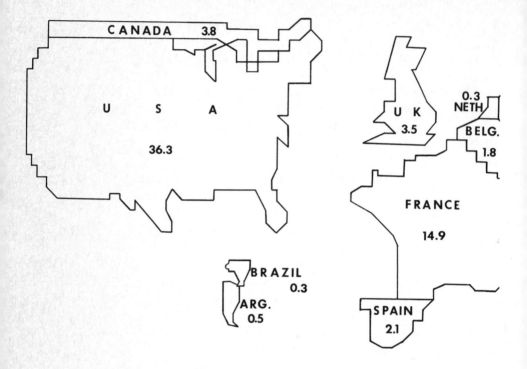

Within a few years, the whole picture of energy economics in the U.S. began to change radically. The second oil shock, which followed the overthrow of the Shah of Iran in 1979, and which saw a complete cutoff of Iranian oil shipments to the U.S., accelerated the process. As the price of OPEC crude climbed to $40 a barrel, American energy consumers reacted to the staggering prices by conserving fuel in a way that had never been imagined. By the end of the decade, demand for electricity had slowed dramatically. In 1980 the demand increased by only 1.7 percent.[18]

The whole electric power business was becoming unraveled. But the utilities did not seem to realize it. In the years immediately following the first oil shock, U.S. power companies ordered a total of twenty-two new reactors with a capacity of 28,000 megawatts. Without realizing it, they were setting themselves up for a fall.

The oil shocks were not, though, the only problem to plague the nuclear power industry during the decade of the seventies. The

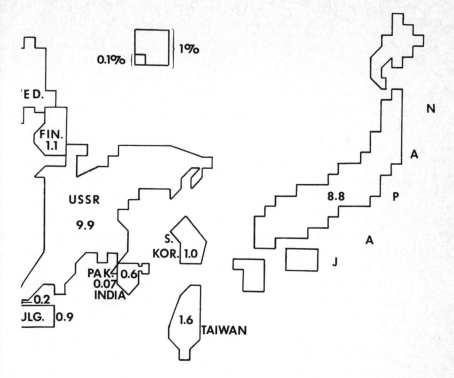

0.1%   1%

ED.

FIN.
1.1

USSR

9.9

S.
KOR. 1.0

PAK. 0.6
0.07
INDIA

≤0.2

JLG. 0.9

1.6
TAIWAN

N

A

8.8   P

A

J

Atoms Around the World. The U.S. gets only 13 percent of its electricity from the atom, but it still uses more nuclear energy than any other country in the world. The map above shows the nuclear nations of the world, their sizes distorted to reflect the proportion of the world's atomic energy each generates and uses.
(Map by Michael Stoler)

midseventies, and the year 1976 in particular, found the antinuclear movement gaining strength and, in some instances, actually taking the offensive in the battle for safer reactors—or for none at all.

The advance of the antinuclear forces had been fueled by the publication of the Rasmussen Report, which delineated the potentially disastrous consequences of a nuclear accident. It picked up momentum as a series of nuclear plant mishaps suggested that reactors were not being run as well as they should be. But what really got the antinuclear forces rolling were the resignations, during 1976, of several long-time nuclear engineers, who not only questioned the whole concept of nuclear plant safety, but came over to the opposition and brought their expertise with them.

The first of the resignations occurred in January of that year when

Robert Pollard, a thirty-five-year-old electrical engineer with the NRC, announced his conversion. Pollard, who had been one of forty-eight project managers at the agency, had been in charge of conducting safety reviews at a number of nuclear power plants, including Consolidated Edison of New York's plants at Indian Point, just north of New York City. He resigned, he said, because of frustration over the NRC's lack of interest in plant safety, and in doing so, he gave both the agency and the people in the Greater New York area some cause for thought. In his letter of resignation, which was released to the press and widely quoted, he said that after reviewing the design of the Indian Point reactors he had come to the conclusion that nothing but "sheer good luck" had prevented an accident from occurring at the three-plant site.[19]

The shock waves from Pollard's resignation had barely abated when, a month later, three senior engineers resigned from GE's nuclear division in California and announced that they were joining the antinuclear cause. One of their number, Dale Bridenbaugh, fueled the antinuclear fires by revealing that he had become increasingly alarmed at the technological shallowness of both the engineers who conceived current nuclear plant design and the regulators who approved them. He described nuclear power as a technological monster, and questioned whether anyone—especially the NRC—was actually in control of the industry.[20]

By autumn of that year, another NRC engineer had also resigned. Ronald Fluegge charged that the NRC had either "covered up or brushed aside nuclear safety problems of far-reaching significance." He also expressed the opinion that many plants were being allowed to operate, and in populated areas, despite "known safety deficiencies" that could result in serious accidents.[21]

The impact of these resignations on the nuclear industry was enormous. Throughout the sixties and early seventies, the AEC, the NRC, and the industry had all been able to dismiss antinuclear groups as emotional flower children or as campus upstarts looking for something, anything, against which they could protest. Nor had the industry found it any more difficult to dismiss or downplay the criticism of biologists who feared the effects of radiation or the handful of physicists who opposed nuclear power out of fear of nuclear proliferation.

But industry leaders and other nuclear advocates found it harder to shrug off the criticism of engineers who had once been the mainstays of the industry, who had initially become involved with nuclear power because they believed in it and felt that the technology was manageable. After all, if the people who worked directly with nuclear power were not aware of its faults, then who could be?

The press, as expected, devoted considerable space to the engineers' resignations and their attacks on the credibility of the nuclear power industry. But the mass media were not the only outlets to see the significance of this crack in nuclear power's once unbroken facade. The industry journal *Nucleonics Week* carried a story headlined, "Four Resignations Radically Change Complexion of Nuclear Fight."

The impact of the resignations was increased when the resignees began appearing at news conferences and hearings of bodies like the Joint Committee on Atomic Energy. Pollard described the problems at Indian Point in chilling detail, mentioning cracked pipes and questioning whether they could stand the strains of providing water to a reactor that had lost its coolant. The former GE engineers produced a list of the defects they had found in their firm's reactors, including leaking seals, sticking valves, unpredictable vibrations, and corroded plumbing. The company and the NRC both issued detailed rebuttals of the trio's charges, maintaining that some problems had never existed and noting that others had either been solved or were in the process of being studied so they could be corrected.

But the rebuttals proved less effective than the engineers' charges, which stressed not the individual things that could go wrong, but the cumulative flaws in nuclear plant design and construction. The public got the message: no nuclear plant could be made perfectly safe. And the public raised a question: were the nuclear plants as built safe enough? Had the companies and the NRC really taken all the steps possible to reduce accidents to remote probabilities, or were they doing only enough to reduce the most obvious risks and trusting to luck to prevent truly serious accidents?[22]

The resignations, and the evidence they provided of dissension within the ranks of the nuclear power industry, gave the antinuclear forces the ammunition they needed to mount a major assault on the atom. By 1976 antinuclear critics managed to force questions on nuclear power onto the ballots in six states. In a way, it did not matter that none of the referenda passed, or even that the most successful was defeated by a margin of two to one. Nuclear advocates cited the defeat of the referenda as a victory over the irrational fear of the atom being spread by a handful of antinuclear types. But they were not able to take much comfort from the votes. For the antinuclear forces' mere success in getting the issues onto the ballots showed their growing strength and gave the industry good reason to believe that its popularity was waning and that it was no longer seen as the source that would provide the solution to America's energy problems. The antinuclear movement had evolved from a force that could be easily dismissed to one that could no longer be ignored.

The extent of the antinuclear feeling was obvious. Antinuclear action had once been limited to petitioning and occasional picketing. By the midseventies, it had escalated into attempts to block plant accesses and occasional acts of civil disobedience. The movement, too, had grown from local groups opposed to particular plants to regional and national coalitions. Buoyed by the fact that they were winning more and more technical converts, the antinuclear forces began to scale up their protests, from demonstrations involving hundreds to actions involving thousands.

The first of these "cast-of-thousands" productions took place in 1975 in Germany. It began in February when a few hundred residents of Whyl, a small village in the Rhineland's wine country, occupied the site on which a 1,350-megawatt nuclear plant was being built. The protesters had demonstrated out of concern for their livelihoods. They feared that the extra humidity caused by the plant's cooling system would change the weather in the area and have an adverse effect on their vines.

The demonstration might have gone off peacefully and ended of its own volition had the protesters been left alone. But the German government, unused to political demonstrations of this type, helped make it into a much bigger affair. When the protesters refused to move and allow construction work to continue, the German police responded with water cannons and arrests. Their action did more than reinforce the Whyl residents in their determination to oppose the plant. The headlines it generated brought in protesters from all over Germany as well as from France. More than 90,000 Germans signed petitions opposing the proposed reactor. More than 20,000 eventually joined the original protesters, who succeeded in occupying the construction site for a year and, in a final victory, halting the construction of the plant. Once again, as they had done at Bodega Bay, California, the antinuclear forces won.[23]

The Whyl protest provided a model for others, including one that took place in New Hampshire in 1977. The point at issue there was a plant with twin 1,150-megawatt reactors that New Hampshire's utility, the Public Service Company, had been planning to build on the Granite State's truncated coastline near the small town of Sea-brook. Public Service planned to use seawater to cool the plant, sucking up about a billion gallons a day and sending it back into the Atlantic about thirty degrees warmer than it was before it was pumped out.

Except for Public Service, few were enthusiastic about the idea. Local clam diggers and lobstermen feared that the warmer waters would affect marine life and cut their catches. Local environmentalists objected that the presence of the plant would disturb the waterfowl that nested and bred in Seabrook's marshes. Geologists pointed out that the proposed plant site straddled a fault line. Potential electricity consumers noted that even before construction got under way, the cost of the plant had doubled, rising to almost $2.5 billion.

But these arguments carried little weight with Public Service, which had been planning the plant for a decade and which had won NRC approval for its plans in 1966. So, in April 1977, the local antinuclear group, a loose coalition of environmentalists, fishermen, and others known as the Clamshell Alliance, carried out a well-planned demonstration. The objective of the alliance was straightforward. It planned to occupy Seabrook's parking lot and block the gates leading to the construction site. The strategy was intended to attract public attention, not destroy the plant. Organized with almost military precision, the demonstrators were cautioned against acts of violence and warned to keep their protest peaceful.

The two thousand or so who showed up for the demonstration did just that. Approaching the plant by road and, on its seaward side, by boat and by a hot, unpleasant march through the marshes, the demonstrators ringed the plant, chanting slogans and waving signs. The demonstration might have been a one-day affair, generating no more than a single page-one story in the Boston papers and a small inside story or two in papers in New York and Chicago, had the demonstrators been allowed to voice their opposition and then go home. Instead, it became a major media event.

What transformed it was the decision by New Hampshire's Governor Meldrim Thomson, a political conservative as well as an ardent backer of Public Service's plans to build nuclear plants, to order the demonstrators arrested. Backed by National Guardsmen, New Hampshire state police arrested more than 1,400 of the demonstrators, roughing more than a few of them up in the process. The arrests assured the Clamshell Alliance and its supporters the coverage they might not otherwise have gotten, guaranteeing them footage on evening television news programs and inch upon inch of space in newspapers across the country. The action of the demonstrators following their arrests kept the story alive for nearly two weeks. More than half of the demonstrators refused to post bond, forcing New Hampshire, which lacked the jail facilities to hold them, to detain them in National Guard armories. "The governor was the best friend we ever had," said one of the demonstration's organizers as he reviewed the television and newspaper coverage that put Seabrook on the map. "We couldn't have done it without him." [24]

Other nuclear opponents felt the same way. But few regarded protesting against the construction of nuclear power plants as a lark. A handful of antinuclear activists were, to be sure, young people who simply wanted to be against something. A few were guilt-ridden liberals unable to make the distinction between nuclear weapons and nuclear power. But most of those opposed to nuclear power acted out of the conviction that the plants were unnecessary and uneconomical. And almost all acted out of the conviction that nuclear power plants, designed, operated, and regulated as they were, were unsafe. They protested in the belief that the benefits of nuclear power in no way justified the risks that the public was being asked to accept. Their belief was reinforced by the message now being preached by the engineers known as the GE Three. The message was nothing if not chilling. After resigning, the three had submitted testimony to the JCAE that concluded with these words: "The cumulative effect of all defects and deficiencies in the design, construction and operation of nuclear power plants makes a nuclear power plant accident, in our opinion, a certain event." [25]

The question, they said, is not whether a nuclear plant accident would occur. The question, they declared, is when and where? It was a question that would soon be answered.

Six

A Rude Awakening

It is one of the best-known of all physical laws. It is known as Murphy's Law, and it is nothing if not simple. It says: "If anything can go wrong, it will."

Attributed to a mythical engineer named Edsel Murphy, the law, like a theme of Paganini, can be expressed in an almost infinite number of variations. Applied to the fields of prototyping and production, it states that "any wire cut to length will be too short." Applied to mathematics, it holds that "any error that can creep in will. It will be in the direction that will do most damage to the calculation." Applied to construction and repair, it declares that "a dropped tool will land where it can do the most damage." Applied to the field of general engineering, it says that "the more innocuous a design change appears, the further its influence will extend."[1]

Few events illustrate the applicability of Murphy's Law better than the one that occurred on the morning of March 28, 1979, at Three Mile Island, a narrow strip of scrub-covered soil a stone's throw from the east bank of the Susquehanna River a few miles downstream from the Pennsylvania state capital at Harrisburg. In the hours before dawn, the engineers operating Metropolitan Edison Company's 900-megawatt TMI Unit 2 were shocked out of somnolence by the ringing of alarm bells as reactor pressures began to rise and the coolant level to fall. Before the sun rose, their actions and the flaws in the plant's design and equipment brought the plant closer to a meltdown than anyone cared to contemplate and transformed what might—what should—have been a routine turbine trip into the worst nuclear power plant accident in history. For five full days, as NRC officials and engineers scratched their heads and let their actions and contradictory statements attest to their bafflement, the plant, which had released at least some radioactive gases and materials into the atmosphere, teetered on the brink of disaster. For five days Pennsylvania's governor and civil defense officials pressed the NRC for advice on whether they should begin to evacuate people from the area. For five days the state of Pennsylvania, not to mention the rest of the U.S. and people elsewhere around the world, held their breath, watched, and waited until TMI-2 was brought under control.[2]

The TMI accident killed no one, at least not outright. The plant did not blow up, melt down, or cause people to glow in the dark, though the accident did generate a certain amount of mordant humor, some of which could be seen in some souvenir T-shirts put on sale shortly after the accident. The shirts showed a sketch of the island's familiar hourglass-shaped cooling towers and bore the legend: "I survived TMI—I think." The accident was not anywhere near as bad as it could have been. But it did an enormous amount of damage nonetheless, for it showed people that, the assurances of the nuclear power industry and its regulators to the contrary notwithstanding, accidents—and potentially disastrous accidents at that—were more than just statistical possibilities. They could really happen.

Actually, they had been happening for years. It was simply that the earliest accidents received little public attention. The records of the NRC reveal that literally thousands of minor malfunctions— "transients," in nuclear jargon—have occurred at nuclear power plants in the U.S. and elsewhere since the first nuclear reactors went online. Most of these have, to be sure, posed few hazards to the people actually on the plant sites, none to people outside the installations. Some resulted in the release of small amounts of radiation. But most of the accidents that have occurred at nuclear power plants endangered no one.

Most, that is, for there have been some—far too many as far as critics are concerned—that have endangered people whose only fault was to have been in the area. One of the first occurred in the fall of 1957 at Windscale, England, where the British Atomic Energy Authority operated a plant consisting of a nuclear reactor fueled with magnox-clad uranium cartridges moderated with graphite and cooled by a flow of forced air. One October day, when the plant was operating normally, operators allowed the temperature of the reactor to rise too rapidly. This rapid temperature rise caused the failure of several fuel cartridges. Deprived of its cladding, the exposed uranium fuel burned, sending a variety of fission products up the plant's four-hundred-foot-tall stack and into the atmosphere.

Condensing, a cloud laden with iodine 131 and containing about 20,000 curies* of radioactivity, drifted south from the plant, contaminating the countryside with its fallout. The fallout did not cause any known cases of radiation sickness, but it did cause a major problem because iodine picked up from grasses by grazing cattle accumulates and concentrates in their milk. To guard against the consumption of contaminated milk, British authorities banned the sale of milk produced in a two-hundred-square-mile area for twenty-five days, or until the concentration of radioactive iodine fell to the supposedly "safe" level of 0.1 microcuries per liter of milk. The Windscale accident compromised the credibility of Britain's nuclear agency and its advocates, both of whom had insisted that nuclear power was safe and both of whom had dismissed the possibility of accidents. The accident also cost the British government a bit of money. Dairy farmers in the affected area were compensated for the loss of their income to the tune of $180,000.[3]

There were plenty of other accidents. One of the worst took place on the night of January 3, 1961, at the AEC's testing grounds in Idaho, a vast area the size of the state of Rhode Island. It involved a miniature test reactor called the SL-1 and three men who were performing a procedure that involved standing on top of the reactor and manually raising a control rod.

To those outside the laboratory containing the SL-1, things appeared to be going well; at least things were quiet. But at 9:01 P.M., a radiation alarm began ringing at the AEC fire station a short distance away from the reactor. Responding to the alarm, emergency crews raced to the reactor building. When they arrived, they were greeted by an eerie silence, broken only by the clicking of their instruments, which showed radiation readings running right off the

---

*Named for the researcher Marie Curie, who discovered radiation, a curie is a measure of the amount of radioactivity in nuclear material. One curie of radiation is equal to 3.7×10^{10} nuclear disintegrations per second, or the activity in one gram of radium. Inhaling or swallowing one microcurie (one millionth of a curie) of a long-lived radioactive substance results in 30,000 disintegrations per second in the body, a potentially deadly dose.

scales. The radiation reading at the entrance of the reactor building, in fact, was a startling 500 rads, a level that could produce fatal effects within thirty days.

When the emergency crews entered the building itself, they found readings as high as 1,000 rads—and chaos. The reactor itself was a burned hulk. The men who had been working with it were in even worse shape. One of the operators was dead. One, still alive, died two hours later en route to a hospital.

The body of the third operator was not immediately visible. It took rescue workers awhile to find it, and when they did, they did not like what they found. The body of the third operator was found a full story above the reactor floor, a control rod running through his groin and out his shoulder and pinning him to the ceiling.

Nor was this all emergency crews discovered. They soon found that the bodies of the SL-1's first two victims were so contaminated by radiation that they had to be packed in water, alcohol, and ice and stored in a radiation-proof vault. The body of the third victim, which was not removed from the building for six days, was equally "hot." Twenty days after the accident, the bodies were still in the vault, cooling down.

The official account of the Idaho accident, described euphemistically as the "SL-1 excursion," which makes it sound like some sort of outing, gives the basic facts. It says, for example, that the excursion that resulted in the explosion was caused by "manual withdrawal, by one or more of the maintenance crew, of the control rod blade from the core considerably beyond the limit specified in the maintenance procedures." The report gives other details as well. It notes that of the several hundred people involved in the recovery operations, twenty-two received exposures in the range of 3 to 27 rems (for roentgen equivalent in man) of radiation, but that at least one received 120 rems. (Nuclear plant workers are allowed by law to be exposed to no more than 3 rems a month except in emergencies.) The report also mentions that some gaseous fission products, including radioactive iodine, escaped into the atmosphere and relates that property damage from the accident totaled $4,350,000.

What the report does not describe is the grisly way in which the victims of the accident were interred. Three weeks after the accident, the hands and heads of the victims, which had been completely exposed at the time of the explosion, were still so hot that they had to be severed and buried, not with the victims, but with the radioactive wastes.[4]

The SL-1 was located in a desolate section of the U.S., well away from any large population center. The Enrico Fermi I reactor, the world's first commercial breeder reactor and one of the American utility industry's most ambitious nuclear projects, was located only a short distance from one of the country's largest and most important cities. Built by Detroit Edison Company at Lagoona Beach, Michigan, the Fermi plant was twenty miles from downtown Detroit. An AEC–industry venture intended to demonstrate the feasibility of breeder reactors, the Fermi plant went into operation in 1963 and operated well for two years.

But at 3:09 on the afternoon of October 5, 1966, things began to go wrong at Fermi. The first indication came when radiation alarms in the reactor building began to sound a Class 1 radiation emergency. The alarms came as the reactor staff was raising the power level of the plant in order to test whether temperature anomalies they had noticed earlier would appear again. The operators quickly realized that the flow of coolant in certain parts of the reactor core had become obstructed, causing the core to overheat. And not just by a small amount. The core overheated to the point where a part of it melted, releasing some 10,000 curies of radioactive gases into, first, the coolant, then the containment building.

For weeks, operators and engineers battled to get the reactor under control and cooled down, wondering all the while what had caused the problem and fearful that they might have had a major disaster on their hands. Whether, as one engineer was later quoted in a book by the same title, "We almost lost Detroit" has never been established. Subsequent investigations revealed the cause of the accident: zirconium liners installed as an afterthought in the cooling system had worked loose, fallen to the bottom of the reactor, and partially blocked the flow of coolant. The same investigation revealed that the liners were unnecessary. But the investigation never established that the fuel melting that occurred would have spread until it involved the entire reactor core.

The Fermi reactor was repaired and put back onto line. In 1970, a full seventeen years after the project got under way, Fermi I achieved power for the first time. Its accomplishment, however, was ironic. In 1972 the reactor was shut down again, this time permanently. Detroit Edison had concluded that it could no longer run the reactor economically.[5]

Two years after the Fermi accident, the French had a problem with one of their nuclear reactors. The Saint Laurent reactor near

Orléans was a high-temperature, gas-cooled power reactor whose construction was undertaken by the French national electric power agency, Électricité de France, and completed late in 1968. It was a complicated piece of machinery; since the fuel elements needed to be replaced frequently, a robot fuel-handling machine was installed on top of the reactor to exchange fuel rods without requiring that the plant be shut down.

Shortly after its completion, the plant was being run at half power for testing when operators decided to try a machine-controlled refueling procedure. The procedure went awry. The refueling machine had been programmed incorrectly by an engineer, the human operator ignored warning signals, and a graphite flow restrictor was accidentally loaded into a fuel channel containing active fuel elements. This cut off the flow of coolant, which in turn caused the core to overheat. Some fifty kilograms (110 pounds) of uranium fuel melted and deformed, and radioactive gases were released into the containment building, though not into the atmosphere.

The accident necessitated expensive decontamination of the plant, repairs to the core, and the installation of a fuel-loading system that did not require the use of graphite flow restrictors. It also set the operation of the plant back by two years. It was late 1970 before the Saint Laurent reactor was restarted.[6]

The Saint Laurent accident resulted from what came down, in the end, to a single operator–equipment failure in the plant and showed that experience was essential if individuals—or companies—were to operate nuclear power plants safely. But an event that occurred at the research reactor at Tennessee's Oak Ridge National Laboratory in 1969 demonstrated that even the most experienced, most knowledgeable of operators could encounter problems when they tried to run something as complex as a nuclear reactor. The reactor at Oak Ridge was protected against fuel melting as a result of decay, or residual, heat by the installation of three battery-operated motors designed to drive the coolant pumps at 10 percent of normal operating speed whenever power to the main pump motors was lost. In theory, the system was a good idea. But ideas are really only good if they work, and on November 19, this one did not. That day the reactor was started up and run for five hours without the protection of the emergency backup system. For, unknown to the reactor's operators, not one, but all three battery supplies were discharged. The reactor did not overheat. But it could have, and if something like a loss of coolant had occurred, the operators would have had no backup system to prevent the reactor from going on what nuclear engineers euphemistically call an "excursion."

A subsequent investigation of the incident revealed no fewer than seven independent failures, half of them attributable to human error. A design failure was responsible for a near accident at the AEC's Hanford, Washington, test site the following year. Like most such devices, Hanford's N Reactor was designed with a SCRAM system to shut it down rapidly in the event of a problem—an arrangement to drop the control rods back into the core automatically should the normal rod drive mechanism fail.

But on September 30, 1970, both the primary and backup systems failed. On that day a clogged pump strainer restricted the flow of coolant to the reactor, causing it to overheat and generating a signal to the SCRAM system. The signal went unheeded. Though each of the control rods was driven by its own hydraulic mechanism, none moved into the reactor core to slow and ultimately stop the nuclear reaction.

The reasons for the failure were puzzling. Each of the rods was held out of the reactor by a solenoid magnet in a system designed so that the rod would drop back in should current to the solenoid be interrupted. But, as an investigation revealed, the system had a flaw. The system's control circuit included a group of four diodes, which allowed each rod to be held out of the reactor core while maintenance was performed. But, investigators found, the system was wired in such a way that, should the diodes for one rod be shorted out and the rod switched out of service, then reverse current through the diodes held all the other rods out of the reactor, too, despite the signal for a SCRAM. The reactor's primary shutdown system, in short, was badly designed and unlikely to work. Fortunately, the reactor's secondary system, which was somewhat simpler, did work. The secondary system consisted of a hopper full of neutron-absorbing graphite balls that sat atop the core. The hopper could be opened and the balls dropped into the reactor merely by operating a mechanical, rather than an electrical, linkage. Dropped into the core, the balls brought about a prompt shutdown of the reactor. They also produced a long-term shutdown as well, since the reactor could not be restarted until all the balls, which filled the spaces between the fuel rods and the wall of the reactor vessel, were removed.[7]

Not all nuclear plant accidents, however, center on the nuclear side of the installation. Like complicated machinery of every kind, nuclear plants can also suffer nonnuclear malfunctions.

Few are more aware of this than the Soviets. They built a small, 121-megawatt fast breeder reactor on the Caspian Sea at Shevchenko, both to generate power and to operate a desalinization plant. Like many such designs, the Shevchenko breeder used liquid sodium as the fluid to carry heat from the core to the plant's steam generator. Using liquid sodium in such a reactor makes sense; the molten metal is an excellent conductor and carrier of heat. But using liquid sodium can also be risky, for sodium is highly reactive and burns and explodes on contact with oxygen. It can burn and explode upon contact with water as well, for water contains enough oxygen to combine with the molecules of sodium.

The risks of using sodium were realized one day in 1973, when a leaking pipe allowed several pounds of sodium to come into contact with water. The resulting explosion destroyed much of the plant's plumbing and forced the shutdown of the plant. The Soviets insist that the nuclear side of the Shevchenko plant was never threatened or compromised and claim that the reactor was shut down hurriedly, but without incident. Though they did for years, they no longer deny that the accident occurred. Their early denials were not believed anyway, for Western sources knew that something had happened at the plant almost as soon as the accident occurred. The flash from the sodium explosion was so bright that it was picked up and recorded by a U.S. reconnaissance satellite that happened to be passing over the U.S.S.R. at the time.[8]

An equally serious nonnuclear accident took place two years later at the TVA's Browns Ferry complex in Alabama. This one developed into a nuclear accident as well.

The Browns Ferry accident took place on the morning of March 22, 1975, and began when a fire forced the shutdown of the three-unit facility's two operating reactors, triggered a near panic in the plant's control room, and started the process that could, if allowed to continue, have led to a meltdown. The accident occurred when workmen went down into a cable room beneath the plant's control room and began using sheets of polyurethane foam to eliminate air drafts in a wall opening. Having installed the foam, the workmen decided to check for air flow by holding a lighted candle close to the partition.

Unfortunately, they held the candle too close. The flame ignited the foam and spread quickly to the vinyl insulation covering the electric cables. The workers attempted to extinguish the flames with carbon dioxide and dry chemicals, but failed, and the fire grew to the point that the room's automatic carbon dioxide extinguishers were activated, forcing the workers to evacuate the area. Nor could other plant personnel help. Workers with masks and air tanks entered the cable room and tried to fight the fire. But smoke and heat forced them, too, to flee. Plant officials summoned firemen from the nearby town of Athens for help.

The workers in the cable room were not the only ones dealing with the effects of the fire. Above them, the operators in the control room were facing another set of problems as the fire shut down instruments and safety systems. They began losing control and instrumentation of the two reactors as the fire burned through key cables and made several safety systems inoperative. Thirty minutes after the fire started, Unit 1 lost power and had to be shut down.

Taking the plant off-line, however, proved anything but easy. Since the fire that destroyed the electrical cables had rendered several of the plant's safety systems useless, the plant's operators could not rely on procedures that had become routine to remove the heat generated by the decay of the radioactive elements in Unit 1's core. For some ten hours, plant operators struggled to keep the core of Unit 1 from overheating and worked to prevent the reactor's fuel from melting. They succeeded when a makeshift arrangement was worked out to use a steam-generator-condensate pump to force cooling water into the reactor.

The AEC, the TVA, the nuclear industry, and antinuclear activists all saw the Browns Ferry accident from different perspectives. Like the legendary blind men examining the elephant, each had a different interpretation of what had happened. The NRC report stressed the fact that there had, in fact, been no damage to the reactor itself and that all damage had occurred in the reactor building but outside of the actual containment structure. Both the NRC and the TVA conceded that the plant's emergency core-cooling system had indeed been rendered *hors de combat* by the destruction of the electrical control cables, but insisted that at no time was the ECCS necessary to maintain the integrity of the reactor core during the fire. The TVA said that while it might have used various emergency core-cooling systems to help dissipate the decay heat that remained following the shutdown of the reactor, sufficient alternate systems were also available. In addition, the TVA said that pressure inside the containment never presented a problem; at no time did it rise above

2.2 pounds per square inch, which kept it well below the 50 pounds per square inch that the container vessel was designed to withstand.[9]

Antinuclear critics, predictably, viewed the accident with something akin to alarm. They saw it as a potential disaster, a near meltdown only narrowly averted. David Comey, one of the leaders of the antinuclear effort, called a news conference that attracted a substantial segment of the press. He got himself quoted on television news broadcasts and in *The New York Times* to the effect that the only thing that prevented a core meltdown was good luck. Daniel Ford of the Union of Concerned Scientists took a more technical turn in his comments, noting quite accurately that "safety systems that are supposed to work during emergencies did not work in this case."[10]

Who was right? Was the Browns Ferry accident a minor mishap blown out of proportion by critics and a cooperative press? Or was it a chilling warning that nuclear power plants were inherently unsafe?

In fact, it was neither. As the investigations conducted by the NRC and the TVA revealed, the accident was a good indication of the kinds of things that could go wrong in the array of electrical circuits and plumbing that enables a nuclear plant to operate. It showed that safety systems could easily be compromised, both by mechanical failures and by the thoughtless actions of a member of the plant staff. It showed that certain materials should not be used in certain parts of a nuclear plant, and it pointed up the need for additional redundancy in plant safety systems.

But the accident also showed that alternative arrangements could be made to cool down a reactor once it had been taken off-line and proved that these arrangements could be effective. At no time did the temperature in Unit 1's core reach dangerous levels. At no time was the accident as bad or the situation at Browns Ferry as dangerous as many critics claimed.

But at no time was the Browns Ferry accident anything that should be casually dismissed. It did not, as the Atomic Industrial Forum would later claim, prove that nuclear plant safety systems would work during an emergency. It showed instead that nuclear plants, because they could not simply be switched off like oil- or coal-fired plants, were particularly vulnerable to all types of accidents.

Through 1978 the nuclear industry and the NRC continued to insist that nuclear power was safe. Both conceded that accidents had occurred, of course, but both also insisted that the accidents were insignificant. Discounting the SL-1 accident, which had, after all, taken place at an experimental government installation rather than a commercial nuclear power plant, NRC and industry spokesmen responded to criticism by noting that no one had ever been killed in a nuclear power plant accident in the U.S. and by reminding critics that no one not actually on the site of any U.S. nuclear plant accident had even been exposed to undue amounts of radiation.

These claims allowed both the NRC and the industry to keep their credibility. A substantial segment of the press still supported nuclear power, not because it was nice, but because, in their considered view, it was necessary. In a 1978 essay, *Time* condemned what it described as "The Irrational Fight Against Nuclear Power," credited nuclear power plants with helping the U.S. to make it through the storms and the coal strike of the previous winter, and endorsed the construction of more reactors. The magazine restated its call a month later after seeing evidence that the U.S.S.R. was getting into nuclear power—and overseas sales of nuclear reactors—in a very big way.[11]

Time was hardly alone. Though many journalists and publications expressed reservations about nuclear power and called continually on the NRC to improve its inspection procedures and insist that nuclear power plants be built and operated safely, few joined in the antinuclear opposition's call to close down all reactors. The press's attitude, however, was soon to change.

The circumstances of the change could hardly be more ironic. On March 16, 1979, a film titled *The China Syndrome* opened at theaters in New York and elsewhere. As a film, it had all the ingredients for success. It starred Jane Fonda, Michael Douglas, and Jack Lemmon. It had a terrific plot: An attractive television newswoman visits a local nuclear plant and witnesses a plant emergency that has the operators in the control room sweating, looking frantically at their gauges and finally, as a gauge shows the water level in the reactor returning to normal, all but collapsing in relief. Her investigations reveal that the plant has just undergone a flirtation with a meltdown. The newswoman's questions also touch the conscience of one of the plant's engineers, who reviews construction records and finds that much of the data has been faked. The plant, it quickly becomes obvious, is unsafe. Worse, its builders and owners know that it is unsafe but, out of greed, venality, arrogance, refuse to acknowledge the dangers and conspire to keep the plant operating, even if they must attempt to kill someone who knows and is willing to tell the truth.

Tense and well-paced, the film made much of the fact that an accident at the plant could be disastrous. At one point, one of the actors even says that, if the plant should melt down, it would "contaminate an area the size of the state of Pennsylvania."

At the time of its release, *The China Syndrome* seemed more entertaining than prophetic. Few denied that the movie had managed to keep them on the edges of their seats. But many pointed out that what had happened in the fictitious plant was almost astronomically unlikely to happen in a real nuclear power plant. The likelihood that any one of the things that went wrong with the plant in the film might happen at an actual plant was small enough. The likelihood that *all* of the things that went wrong in the film could happen in real life was even smaller. And finally, the likelihood that *all* of the things that went wrong in the cinematic plant could happen in a real plant *in the sequence they did* and thus cause a meltdown were even smaller than that.

The film cast suspicion on power company executives and government bureaucrats alike. But an action that took place the week after the film opened suggested that maybe the NRC was doing a little better job than the movie's producers realized. For, in a surprise move, the NRC ordered five plants—Maine Yankee in Wiscasset; the James A. Fitzpatrick plant in Scriba, New York; Surry 1 and 2 in Gravel Neck, Virginia; and the Beaver Valley plant in Shippingport, Pennsylvania—shut down after questions were raised about their ability to withstand earthquakes.

The NRC's order to turn off the plants, which together produced around 4.1 million kilowatts of electric power, did not mean that the installations were unsafe. It meant, said the NRC, that it wanted to make sure they were safe. Engineers from Pennsylvania's Duquesne Power and Light, which operated Shippingport, and from the Boston firm of Stone and Webster, which had designed all five plants, had discovered a mathematical defect in the computer program used to design some of the plants' coolant pipes so they would be strong enough to withstand a major earthquake, something that had not occurred in the East since a serious quake hit Charleston, South Carolina, in 1886. The firms promptly reported their discovery to the NRC, which ordered the shutdown until a new computer analysis could be undertaken.[12]

The NRC action might have reassured a few of those who had not already made up their minds that all nuclear plants should be closed. But what happened the following week ruined any attempts at reassurance the industry might have made. For the accident at Three Mile Island hit the U.S. and its nuclear power industry with all the force of an exploding bomb, blasting away the credibility of both the industry and its regulators. It changed forever the widespread view that nuclear plants posed no real threat to the public.

That the accident occurred in Pennsylvania was itself accidental. The giant General Public Utilities, which owned both Jersey Central Power and Light Company and Pennsylvania's Metropolitan Edison Company, had originally planned to build a second plant at Oyster Creek. But labor troubles, intimations that a shakedown was coming, and threats of huge cost overruns, all of which have long plagued all kinds of construction projects in New Jersey, made company officials wonder if they really wanted to take on such problems. Deciding that the answer was no, GPU asked the NRC if it could build the same plant, a Babcock and Wilcox pressurized water reactor, at Three Mile Island, where another B&W reactor was already in operation. The NRC approved the switch, and GPU went ahead with the plant, despite the fact that the blueprints had to be redrawn and the reactor building rotated 90 degrees so that it would mate with existing structures on the island.[13]

The reactor had been operating for about a year, and was up and running at 97 percent of capacity on the morning of March 28. People of the area had become accustomed to the way the plant's huge, hourglass-shaped cooling towers dominated the landscape. They had even become accustomed to hearing the alarm bells on the island as the plant experienced minor malfunctions or as the staff conducted safety drills. So no one off the island heard—or thought—anything amiss as the hands of the clock moved slowly toward the hour of 4:00 A.M.

But Fred Scheimann, one of the operators, did. Shortly before 4:00, he had descended eight flights into the bowels of the turbine building, hoping that he could figure out a way to clear up a problem in one of the steam generator's filter tanks, where the resin balls used to filter the water had become stuck together. He had just climbed atop a huge pipe to get a better look at a gauge when his ears detected, first, silence, which meant that a pump had shut down, and then a noise that sent chills down his spine. The noise was like that made by an express train. It was the sound made by a slug of steam rushing through a pipe. Scheimann heard it just in time. He leaped clear only a fraction of a second before the pipe on which he had been standing was ripped from its mounting, tearing out valves and releasing a spray of scalding water.[14]

A second later things began to go crazy in the control room. Alarm bells began ringing. Alarm lights began flashing. Supervisor Bill Zewe, a veteran of the Navy's nuclear program, rushed from his office in time to grab the intercom and tell the sixty or so people at work on the island as much as he knew. He announced that TMI Unit 2 had tripped and was shutting itself down.

It took operators a while to figure out what had happened. But eventually, they managed to piece things together. What had happened was that a pump failed in the reactor's secondary loop, which carries nonradioactive water into the plant's steam generator, where it absorbs heat generated by the nuclear chain reaction in the reactor core from the plant's radioactive primary loop. Normally, this nonradioactive water is turned into steam that drives the turbine and generates electricity. With no steam to push it, though, the turbine had shut down.

Turbine trips are routine occurrences at nuclear—and other— power plants. But they pose an extra problem at nuclear plants, for the steam does more than merely power the turbine. The steam also helps remove heat from the water that is cooling the reactor core. Without steam in its steam generators, the coolant in a nuclear plant can heat up, expand, and build up a dangerous level of pressure in the reactor core. When this happens, the plant's first safety system, a relief valve at the top of the core, is supposed to open automatically, releasing the excess pressure.

This is what happened at Three Mile Island. Unfortunately, it is not all that happened. For the relief valve on TMI-2 was small—too small, in fact, to release all the pressure necessary to prevent the reactor's coolant from overheating. So the plant's second automatic safety device, the SCRAM, dropped the control rods into the reactor core—or tried to. Propelled by small charges of nitrogen, the control rods were thrust into the core so fast that several of them bent and jammed. Those that were in place could not stop the reactor from producing heat. Because nuclear decay continues even after the main chain reaction has been stopped, the reactor continued to produce heat at the rate of about 6 percent of normal capacity.[15]

In theory, the overheated coolant should have lost its heat, albeit slowly. But in fact, that is not what happened. The relief valve atop the core was supposed to have closed down again thirteen seconds into the accident, when the pressure in the reactor returned to normal. Had this happened, the closing would have prevented undue loss of core coolant. But it did not happen, and the plant's operators were unaware of the fact. A light on the control panel showed that the electric current that had opened the valve had been switched off, leading the operators to believe that the valve had closed. In fact, the valve had stuck in the open position. Worse, it would remain open for two hours and twenty minutes, draining the vital coolant from the reactor and causing plant operators to lose valuable time looking elsewhere for the cause of the coolant loss. Within five minutes of the initial turbine trip, some 32,000 gallons of coolant escaped. Before the problem was discovered, more than 250,000 gallons of radioactive water would flow out of the reactor and collect on the containment building floor.[16]

The jammed relief valve, though, was only one of the problems confronting TMI-2's operators as they struggled to bring the reactor under control. Operator errors were compounding their mechanical problems. One of the errors was procedural. The plant's operating manual warned operators that a pipe temperature of 200 degrees or more indicated an open valve. But the operators either did not look or failed to take note of the temperatures in the pipes, which recorders show reached 285 degrees. Instead, they said later that temperatures at the plant routinely registered high because some valve was always leaking.

These errors and others caused the upper part of the reactor's core to become uncovered. The lack of covering caused the core to overheat. In fact, the core did more than just overheat. It began to overheat rapidly. Its temperature soared to the point where the fuel rods' zirconium-alloy cladding began to melt and deform, and that was high indeed. Zirconium is highly heat-resistant and does not begin to melt until its temperature exceeds 3,000 degrees. Zirconium has another peculiar property, too. It can react with steam to produce hydrogen. And hydrogen, as anyone who has read about the *Hindenburg* disaster knows, possesses an interesting property of its own. It can combine with oxygen to produce an explosion.[17]

The possibility of a hydrogen explosion (and a minor one actually did occur in the reactor the afternoon of the accident) was not, however, the plant operators' primary concern during the early hours of March 28. Heat was. The core was heating up at a staggering rate. If it reached a temperature of 5,200 degrees, it would melt through the bottom of the reactor vessel and drop into the water-filled sump in the containment building. If it did that, several things could happen. The white-hot core could cause the water in the sump to flash off as steam, which could rupture the containment and release a radioactive cloud. Or it could cause the water to boil off more slowly, though without giving up much heat of its own, and melt its way through the floor of the reactor building and into the ground, causing another cloud of radioactive steam the moment it came into contact with groundwater.

Either way, the results would be disastrous. A cloud of radioactive materials would drift downwind, causing radiation sickness, latent cancers, and all the other problems about which scientists warned in WASH-740 and the later Rasmussen Report. The plant would not, to be sure, explode like a bomb. But the effects on people in the path of the radioactive cloud would be little different from those caused by a nuclear blast.

By 6:00 A.M., two hours after the accident had started, Zewe had a good idea as to what was going on at TMI-2 and a good idea as to how bad the situation had become. He picked up the intercom mike and announced, in a voice that echoed through every speaker on the island, "This is Unit Two. We are declaring a site emergency. This is not a drill." As he put down the microphone, Zewe flipped the alarm switch. Warning horns and klaxons shrilled over the island.[18]

But even before the alarms sounded, everybody on the island knew that something unusual was under way, and most were working frantically to do something—anything—about the problem. They, at least, were trying to solve it. Off the island, officials of the Metropolitan Edison Company were also involved in an exercise in damage control. They were trying to contain the problem, and in an attempt to do so, they launched a public relations campaign to convince the public that there was no real crisis and that whatever crisis there was would soon be over. The plant had undergone a routine turbine trip, they said early on the morning of March 28; it was undergoing a routine shutdown and there was no cause for concern. "There have been no recordings of any significant levels of radiation and none are expected outside the plant," said Met Ed's chief spokesman, Don Curry, shortly after the site emergency was declared. "The reactor is being cooled according to design by the reactor cooling system and should be cooled by the end of the day. There is no danger of a meltdown. There were no injuries, either to plant workers or to the public." Said another company spokesman, David Klucsick: "We are not in a China Syndrome situation." [19]

This statement turned out, like other company statements, to be somewhat less than honest. For it quickly became clear that Met Ed itself was not only unsure as to the seriousness of the accident at its plant but compounding its uncertainty by trying to downplay those facts it did know. What made this evident was the fact that shortly after the company released its initial reassuring statement, officials of Pennsylvania's Department of Environmental Resources flew over the plant in a helicopter carrying a Geiger counter. The instrument, they reported, detected a "small release of radiation into the environment."

What was going on? Confronted with this finding, Curry and other company officials backpedaled and offered a new explanation. When the secondary loop lost pressure and the turbine stopped, they said, pressure and temperature both rose in the primary loop. This, in turn, opened several relief valves, allowing some radioactive water to leak onto the floor of the reactor building. How, then, did the radioactive steam escape from the reactor building? Again, company officials offered an explanation. The control rods had been reinserted into the core, stopping the nuclear chain reaction. But the loss of water allowed the core to overheat anyway. Water pumped into the system caused the pressure to rise and other relief valves to open. These valves allowed some radioactive steam to escape out the top of the containment building dome, and when the temperature of the reactor core continued to rise, plant engineers vented some more steam to keep it from rising too high. In addition, explained company officials, some of the radioactive water that spilled from the plant's primary loop was automatically drawn from the containment building floor into the neighboring auxiliary building, which was not designed to handle radioactive materials. The water gave off xenon and krypton gases that were pumped through the building's ventilation system and out into the atmosphere.

How much radiation was there? Company officials said at first that they did not know. A nuclear engineer who had flown in the state helicopter had measured the radiation level downwind of the plant at 1 millirem an hour, a level that could not be considered dangerously high. Later that afternoon, company president Walter Creitz put the radiation levels at the perimeter of the two-hundred-acre plant site at a nonthreatening 2 to 3 millirems per hour.

But, given the different stories that were being disseminated by plant engineers and company officials, neither the press, nor the public, nor local officials were willing to believe much from Met Ed. At an acrimonious news conference, Mayor Robert Reid of Middletown, the community just across the river from the plant, angrily asked why the company was hesitating about disclosing the dangers faced by residents of the town. Reporters, meanwhile, concentrated their fire on Jack Herbein, the company's vice president for power generation. He made a perfect target. Speaking in technical jargon, he went out of his way to avoid calling what had happened at Three Mile Island an accident. Instead, he referred to the turbine trip as a "transient," a term that made journalists wonder if he was referring to someone with no fixed abode. He also managed to describe what had happened at the plant as a "normal aberration," which sounded like something out of Krafft-Ebing, and "not a normal evolution," which made reporters wonder if they should not be reading Darwin. (Later that week, when asked what might happen if hydrogen believed to be building up in the reactor should come into contact with a spark, Herbein delivered himself of a howler. He said that the result could well be "spontaneous energetic disassembly" of the reactor. When reporters asked the difference between this process and an explosion, he angrily declined to answer additional questions.) Badgered by reporters and local officials, and sweating profusely under the lights set up by television crews, Herbein finally lost his temper. "Look," he said, trying to put across the company's position, "we didn't injure anybody. We didn't overexpose anybody. We didn't kill a single soul."[20]

The press and the public both panned Met Ed's performance, which suggested that the company was far more worried about the cost of cleaning up after the accident and the costs of keeping the plant off-line than it was about public safety. Herbein refused to dismiss the possibility that the company's customers would be asked to pay the cost of decontaminating the two buildings affected by the accident.

Meanwhile, the NRC, which had arrived on the scene, found itself contradicting the company by reporting that it had detected radioactivity as far as sixteen miles from the plant and revealing that radiation levels within the containment building had soared to a searing 1,000 rems. By Thursday NRC officials were describing the plant failure as "one of the most serious nuclear accidents to occur in the U.S." They were also trying to respond to questions from

Pennsylvania Governor Richard Thornburgh, who had suggested that pregnant women and children leave an area within a five-mile radius of the plant, and who wanted to know whether he should order a general evacuation of the area.

The public was not reassured by the news coming from the crippled plant. On Thursday Creitz conceded that similar incidents had happened earlier at TMI's Unit 1, which had been shut down for routine refueling at the time of the accident, but that in these instances the tanks had not overflowed. At this time, too, company officials revealed that some of the reactor's fuel rods had been damaged when the core became uncovered early in the accident. Met Ed said that less than 1 percent of the reactor's 37,000 fuel rods had been damaged. After doing some checking of their own, however, NRC officials upped the estimate to 60 percent.[21]

By Friday the public's credulousness was stretched to the breaking point by the news that additional releases of radioactive steam were coming from the plant. The releases, like those that had taken place earlier, were accidental. According to NRC investigators, plant workers had been trying to remove some radioactive water from the pump building. But as the water flowed into a storage tank, the temperature and pressure both began to climb, causing a valve to open and allowing the gases to escape into the building. There, they were sucked up by the ventilation system and blown out a stack—just, as Met Ed's luck would have it, as a federal–state monitoring crew flew by in a small plane.

The releases triggered hysterical reports of "uncontrolled radiation" and a debate between the various parties dealing with and covering the accident as to whether the release had been accidental or deliberate. The questions, meanwhile, led to the disclosure that the reactor was not cooling down, as company officials had been telling the public, but was remaining stubbornly at 280 degrees. Nor were these the only disturbing disclosures to come from the NRC's compound of trailers across the river from Three Mile Island that day. There were also indications—which later proved false—that a bubble of hydrogen gas had developed inside the reactor. The existence of such a bubble could have posed several problems. One was the obvious danger of an explosion. The other was that the bubble, sitting on top of the core like a lid on a pressure cooker, could maintain abnormally high temperatures within the reactor and in addition prevent the flow of water necessary to cool the core down.[22]

NRC and company engineers spent most of Friday discussing

various ways of getting rid of the suspected hydrogen bubble. On Saturday they did something, venting steam from the containment building to reduce pressures, but in the process, releasing more radioactive gas into the atmosphere. As they did, people in the area packed their cars with clothes, and the governor and his staff continued to plan for an evacuation they hoped—successfully, it turned out—to be unnecessary.

Saturday was a tense day at Three Mile Island and in the area surrounding the plant. The tension was not eased by the fact that *The China Syndrome* was playing at a theater less than fifteen minutes' drive from the crippled nuclear plant. The Saturday night screenings of the film were packed by locals, some of whom called out remarks comparing Met Ed's Herbein and Creitz with the power company executives depicted so unflatteringly in the movie. The audience at one showing, in fact, got quiet only once during the show—when the nuclear plant engineer who turns out to be one of the film's heroes warns that an accident could contaminate an area the size of Pennsylvania. That line hit close, too close, to home, and the audience gasped when it heard it.

On Sunday President Jimmy Carter, a one-time U.S. Navy nuclear engineer, helicoptered from Washington to Middletown, where he donned yellow plastic boots and toured the plant for a briefing on what had happened and what was being done to end TMI-2's excursion and bring it back under control. The NRC determined that the hydrogen bubble—if it had actually existed—was gone. Radiation monitors spotted around the area revealed that radiation levels had returned to normal. The reactor itself was stable and cooling down, though too slowly to make anyone involved with it feel completely at ease. Governor Thornburgh heaved a sigh of relief at the realization that an evacuation would be unnecessary, and the 100,000 or so of the area's 650,000 residents who had fled—many of them to cots set up in an auditorium at an amusement park in nearby Hershey—began to return to their homes. The crisis at Three Mile Island was over.[23]

But much work remained to be done. The reactor still needed to be cooled to the point that officials could declare a "cold shutdown" and allow NRC engineers and plant workers to begin the monumental task of cleaning up the mess and decontaminating the reactor and auxiliary buildings. An investigation had to be launched to determine what had happened, to review the design and the mechanical and human failures that had caused and contributed to the accident, and to determine what could be done to see that they did not happen again. And the nuclear power industry, which had allowed its own handling of the accident to destroy in days such credibility as it had managed to build up over a period of years, had to take stock of itself and see what it could learn from its terrifying experience.

The week after the accident was spent in installing new plumbing so that a process of natural circulation could be used to cool down the reactor and get the temperature of its coolant down to a safe 200 degrees or less. It was also spent in assessing the damage to the plant, which was considerable. Robert M. Bernero, an NRC expert on nuclear plant decommissioning, estimated that the cost of cleaning up the plant could easily come to more than the $700 million GPU had spent to build TMI-2 in the first place.

President Carter used the week following the accident to appoint what turned out to be only one of several panels to investigate what had happened. The President named Dartmouth College President John Kemeny, a noted mathematician who had helped to develop the computer language known as BASIC, to head a twelve-member commission composed of leaders from labor, business, the sciences, and education. The commission was ordered to study the accident, determine what happened and why, and identify the problems, both technical and human, that had contributed to it. Congress and the NRC, meanwhile, launched their own investigations.

But even before the investigations got under way, certain things were obvious. One was that, whether it came close or not, the reactor at Three Mile Island did not, in fact, melt down. But another was that the credibility of both the nuclear power industry and the NRC did.

That realization left both organizations shaken. AIF President Carl Walske spoke for many in the industry when he said, "I thought we were better than that before the accident happened."[24] Ellyn R. Weiss, general counsel for the Union of Concerned Scientists, said that the accident "really shook a lot of people out of their complacency, particularly in the NRC."[25] But it was NRC Commissioner Victor Gilinsky, a Carter appointee and a frequent critic of the nuclear power industry, who best summed up the effect of the accident at Three Mile Island. "What shook the public the most," he said, "was seeing the men in the white lab coats standing around and scratching their heads because they didn't know what to do. The result was that accidents got taken seriously in a way they never had before."[26]

Gilinsky was right. Before Three Mile Island, nuclear accidents were only theoretical hazards, the stuff of movie plots or eventualities conjured up by people in the antinuclear movement to strengthen their philosophical arguments against nuclear power. Before Three Mile Island, nuclear accidents seemed less than real to most people, remote possibilities that might or could happen, but not something likely to happen soon or in the worst way possible.

The accident changed the public's perception about nuclear risks just as dramatically as a miracle changes the faith of those who witness it. It showed that major accidents, accidents that *could* endanger the lives of hundreds of thousands, that *could* meet all the conditions of the Rasmussen Report's worst-case scenario, could really happen. It showed, too, that neither utility company executives nor the NRC really knew how to deal with major mishaps at nuclear power plants. It showed, finally, that the public was not being well protected by the agency that licensed and monitored nuclear power plants, for one of the things that came out early in the period following the accident was that TMI-2 had been plagued with problems since it first went on-line and that neither the company nor the NRC had done much to solve them.

The accident at Three Mile Island did not kill or injure anyone immediately, as company officials were quick to note. But it did kill something. It killed public trust. Americans might have been willing to trust the industry and the NRC before the accident. Now they were suspicious of both. "It's like having your wife catch you in bed with another woman," lamented a utility company executive who viewed the accident from afar. "Even if the marriage stays together, things are never the same again. The faith that makes the relationship work is gone."[27]

It certainly was after Three Mile Island. Any trust that Americans might have had in the industry or its regulator went right up the stack with the radioactive steam released from the damaged nuclear plant.

Seven

The Reasons Why

What happened?

This was the question asked at Three Mile Island. It was asked by the Nuclear Regulatory Commission, by members of Congress, and by the public, both that segment of it that lived in the area surrounding the crippled nuclear plant and the larger segment living elsewhere around the U.S.

What happened?

The question had been asked before, of course. It had been asked at 4:00 A.M. on March 28, when the turbine at Three Mile Island first tripped. It had been asked when the relief valve atop the reactor had stuck in the open position, allowing the core coolant to escape and sending the temperature of the core climbing toward the danger point. It had been asked when systems designed to keep the core covered failed, as radioactive water poured onto the floor of the reactor building and spilled into the plant's auxiliary building. It had been asked as radioactive steam was vented into the crisp Pennsylvania air and as the reading on at least one radiation meter in the plant went right off the scale.

What happened?

The question was asked repeatedly during the week that followed the fateful morning. But it was not fully answered. Engineers from

117

both the Nuclear Regulatory Commission and Metropolitan Edison Company had been too busy trying to figure out what *was* happening and what *could* happen to dissect the Three Mile Island nuclear power station to determine what *had* happened to cause its near destruction.

Once things calmed down a bit, though, everyone turned his attention to the question, and to others as well. For as the public, the President, the NRC, and even Met Ed realized, it was not enough merely to determine what had happened. It was also essential to learn why it had happened and to determine what could and should be done to assure that it would not happen again, either at Three Mile Island or at any of the eighty-plus other nuclear power plants around the country.

The first of the questioners to come up with an answer was Metropolitan Edison, which conducted a quick internal investigation. Just how quick—and how incomplete—the company's investigation was could be quickly seen by anyone who knew anything about nuclear power plants or about what had gone wrong in the plant at Three Mile Island. The tourists who drove through Middletown, Pennsylvania, that summer, headed south, and then stopped to have their pictures taken in front of the plant that had made so much news may have been satisfied by the explanation offered in a fifteen-minute documentary film shown repeatedly at Met Ed's observation center, a modern structure with an excellent view of the plant. The film acknowledged that there had been an accident at TMI-2 and reported that the plant was currently shut down for repairs and decontamination. It also offered a quick explanation as to why the accident had occurred. The accident at Three Mile Island, said the film, had resulted from "a complex combination of equipment failures, ambiguous instruments, and operator failures." But, the film also suggested, the impact of the accident was exaggerated. After all, its narrator noted, the amount of radiation released into the atmosphere was insignificant.[1]

Unfortunately, at least for Met Ed, the film was quickly outdated. The NRC had spent the months immediately following the accident conducting an investigation of its own, going over plant records and instrument recordings, talking to plant personnel and reconstructing the events leading up to and following the turbine trip and had come up with its own response to the questions everyone wanted answered. In August 1979, the NRC released its report.

Based upon hundreds of hours of hearings, the two-inch-thick NRC report offered some comfort to those in the business of designing and building nuclear power plants, including those who had designed and built the plant at Three Mile Island. It stated categorically that although the Pennsylvania plant was not "fail-safe," both its equipment and its emergency procedures were "adequate to have prevented the serious consequences of the accident if they had been permitted to function or be carried out as planned."[2]

Unfortunately, noted the NRC report, they were not. The agency investigation found that the most serious aspects of the accident were due almost entirely to human error. The NRC's investigators found that Metropolitan Edison's operators overrode the plant's automatic safety systems in their attempts to avert the rapidly developing crisis that occurred when the electricity-generating turbine tripped and shut itself—and the plant—down. Those operator actions, said the report, turned what should have been a relatively minor event into a potential disaster. The operators, the NRC investigators concluded, should have kept their hands to themselves and allowed the plant's emergency core-cooling system to work as it was designed to do. Instead, they paid "undue attention" to keeping the coolant from overfilling the reactor and refused to believe instruments that indicated that the plant's uranium core was getting perilously hot.

The release of the report was, as expected, a slap at Metropolitan Edison. But its release did not prevent the NRC itself from taking a slap. The slap came from Congress, which had been conducting its own investigation of the accident. In a report approved by a vote of 29 to 2, the House Subcommittee on Government Operations blasted the NRC's performance in dealing with the accident and the problems that contributed to it. Specifically, the committee criticized the NRC for failing "to demonstrate strong constructive leadership" in developing evacuation plans and related emergency procedures for areas adjacent to nuclear power plants. The committee noted that of the twenty-five states that had nuclear power plants, only sixteen had NRC-approved emergency plans, and sharply attacked the NRC's whole attitude toward safety. The NRC, said one committee staff member, simply "pretended that nuclear accidents could not happen."[3]

An even more scathing report on the accident was soon to come. The twelve-member commission appointed by President Carter and headed by Dartmouth College President John Kemeny had been doing its own study of the accident, and word leaking out of commission headquarters had already indicated that nuclear power proponents who had been hoping that the investigation would attribute what happened at Three Mile Island to a rare, isolated, and possibly unrepeatable sequence of mechanical and human failures were going to be sadly disappointed. Even before it released its report, it was evident that the Kemeny Commission placed the blame for the accident on federal regulators, on the plant's builders, and on the control room operators. Indeed, six of the commission's members had voted to ask President Carter to ban the construction of new nuclear plants until the reforms the commission was about to suggest could be carried out. The request for the moratorium was not made, however. Kemeny, who had supported other calls for a ban in earlier voting, inexplicably decided to abstain when it came to the final ballot. What the commission did do was urge the President to prevent the start of any new construction in any states that did not have approved plans for dealing with a nuclear accident. The ban was academic anyway; no one had attempted either to build a new plant or to start up a new one since the accident. [4]

The Kemeny Commission did its job thoroughly. It took more than 150 depositions and collected enough documents, reports, and testimony to fill more than three hundred feet of library shelves. It also compiled a report that was a paragon of clarity. [5]

Released at the end of October, the Kemeny Commission's report confirmed what a great many had come to suspect: that the much-feared China Syndrome, which some nuclear proponents had dismissed as a virtual impossibility, had indeed been possible at Three Mile Island. The commission calculated that at least thirty tons of the reactor's fuel had become uncovered, overheated, and reached a temperature of 4,000 degrees Fahrenheit or more, suggesting that the reactor was well on its way toward the meltdown point of 5,200 degrees.

Nor was this the only part of the commission's conclusions that had nuclear critics saying, "I told you so." The commission also concluded that technology was not the main problem at Three Mile Island. Though it found that an equipment failure had initiated the chain of events involved in the accident, it concluded that the main problem at Three Mile Island—and, by extension, in the nuclear industry as a whole—was people. The report said: "The most serious mindset is the preoccupation of everyone with the safety of equipment, resulting in the downplaying of the importance of the human element in nuclear power generation." The Kemeny Commission concluded that equipment was important, of course. But, it stressed, equipment alone was not enough to guarantee the safety of those who might be affected by nuclear plant accidents. "We are tempted to say that while an enormous effort was expended to assure that safety-related equipment functioned as well as possible, and that there was back-up equipment in depth," the report said, "what the NRC and the industry have failed to recognize sufficiently is that the human beings who manage and operate the plants constitute an important safety system."[6]

The Kemeny Commission criticized the performance of the people actually operating the Three Mile Island plant at the time of the accident. But it did not hold them solely responsible for all the events that put the plant in the news. As far as the Kemeny Commission was concerned, there was plenty of blame to go around. Some of the blame was directed at General Public Utilities Service Corporation, which built Three Mile Island's two plants. GPU, said the commission, "lacked the staff or expertise to discharge its responsibility" for designing a safe plant. Some of the blame was directed at Metropolitan Edison, to which GPU had given the job of running Three Mile Island. Met Ed, the commission said, "lacked sufficient knowledge, expertise and personnel to operate the plant and maintain it properly."[7]

Some of the blame was directed at the Nuclear Regulatory Commission, which had only a week earlier announced its intention of fining Met Ed $155,000, the maximum permitted by law, for safety violations at Three Mile Island. Though acknowledging that Met Ed's operators met NRC training standards, the commission reported that it had found those standards low and totally "inadequate for responding to the accident." Nor was this the only blame the Kemeny Commission attached to the NRC. The commission also faulted the NRC's performance during the accident, finding that the agency and its personnel had acted "in an atmosphere of uncertainty" and taken actions that it considered "ill-defined."[8]

These were merely the commission's general conclusions. It backed up these general statements with a detailed bill of particulars that did nothing to restore faith in the ability of either the industry or the NRC to assure the public's safety. The commission found, for example, that Three Mile Island's Unit 1, which had been shut down for routine refueling at the time of the accident at Unit 2, had been poorly maintained. Indeed, said the commission, it was so poorly maintained that boron stalactites, some of them a foot long, hung from dripping valves. Both plants, the report noted, had been plagued with leaks and valve problems that should have been corrected but were not, apparently because correcting them would have required that the plants be shut down and forced Met Ed to buy replacement power from some other source. TMI-2's control room, the commission found, was poorly designed, set up so that important gauges and dials were hidden from the operators' view. It was also poorly managed; on the morning of the accident, a large yellow repair tag dangled from one switch, covering a key dial.[9]

The NRC's performance was also criticized in detail. The commission found that the NRC was slow in getting to the scene of the accident and noted that once there, it was overly concerned with the public relations aspects of the mishap. In fact, said the report, at one particularly crucial time, when the NRC should have been concentrating on deciding whether or not it would recommend evacuation of the area, its commissioners allowed themselves to become sidetracked and became "preoccupied with the details of evacuation planning and the drafting of a press release."

But the report's toughest language was directed at the system under which nuclear plant operators were trained. The commission clearly was not impressed by the fact that the Three Mile Island operators had scored above the national average in the testing and licensing examinations administered by the NRC. The NRC's standards for operator training were simply too low. Its tests told little about operators' fundamental understanding of reactors, said the commission, and gave little attention to the biological hazards of radiation. In fact, the commission found, the content of both operator training programs and tests were generally left to the discretion of the instructors, most of whom had no more formal education than their students. Indeed, the commission noted, the NRC had never established a minimum educational requirement for control room operators. The report said: "Fundamental changes will be necessary in the organization, procedures and practices—and above all—in the attitudes of the NRC, and to the extent that the institutions we investigated are typical, of the nuclear industry."[10]

To improve the situation and to prevent an accident like that at Three Mile Island from happening again, the Kemeny Commission came out with no fewer than forty-four recommendations.[11] But only two of them were concerned with the nuts and bolts of nuclear power plant design. The rest were directed at reforming the institutions involved with building, running, or regulating nuclear plants.

The improvements necessary started at the top as far as the commission was concerned. They had to begin with the NRC, which the report described as "a headless agency that lacks the direction and vitality needed to police the nuclear power industry on a day-to-day basis." To correct this condition, the Kemeny Commission recommended abolishing the NRC and replacing it with a single Director of Nuclear Regulation, who would be appointed by and responsible to the President. "When you have a collegial body," said a commission member, "you delay decision-making while searching for the lowest common denominator of agreement." Having a single director, he added, would enable a regulatory agency to move more quickly and leave no doubt in the minds of anyone involved as to where final responsibility for all decisions rested.[12]

One of the first tasks facing any new czar of nuclear regulation, said the report, would have to be the improvement of nuclear plant operator training as well as improvement in the design of the rooms in which these plant operators would work. Operators, said the commission, should be retested regularly.

So should the nuclear plants themselves. The commission recommended that federal licenses allowing utilities to operate nuclear power plants be both reviewable and renewable—as well as suspendable should examination of a company's record or investigation of complaints show that it was operating its plant unsafely. Noting that nuclear plants were licensed once for their forty-year lifetimes, Arizona Governor Bruce Babbit, a pronuclear member of the commission, said: "We must find some way to drive out of the business the utility companies that prove to be incompetent."

In other recommendations, the commission urged that no new nuclear plants be located near large urban centers, that the granting of any new licenses be contingent upon the adoption of workable emergency-response and evacuation plans, and that members of the news media be given enough access to nuclear power plants to become familiar with them and to enable them to do a better job of reporting on them.[13]

Spokesmen for the nuclear power industry knew better than to take issue with either the commission's findings or its recommendations. The AIF's Carl Walske called the report "useful," and other industry leaders conceded that the report had said some necessary things and predicted that it would enable them to make their plants even safer. Most took such comfort as they could find from the fact that nothing in the commission's conclusions suggested that the problems of guaranteeing the safety of nuclear power plants was insoluble. And some of the commission's targets noted that they had already done a bit of soul searching. The NRC, for example, had said in its own report that "everyone connected with nuclear power technology must accept as a fact that accidents can happen. Operations personnel in particular must not have a mind-set that future accidents are impossible. The experience of Three Mile Island has not been sufficient to eradicate that mind-set in all quarters, and the effect of that experience will fade with time. We have no easy answer to suggest, but attitudes must be changed."

The impact of the accident at Three Mile Island and of the reports on why it happened was enormous. The industry reacted to the reports by shelling out a total of $22 million to form two new organizations aimed at improving both reactors and the people who ran them. The Nuclear Analysis Center was a technical institute to study reactor design and to come up with new and better safety equipment; the Institute for Nuclear Power Operations was a center for studying and improving nuclear plant operator training.[14]

The NRC reacted to the accident and the reports with a plethora of new requirements and regulations. In an effort to apply the lessons taught by the accident, it ordered that all nuclear plants, both those under construction and those already in operation, install new safety equipment and backup cooling systems. Industry officials complained that much of this equipment was redundant and unnecessary. But no company refused to comply. The NRC also upgraded its requirements for operator training, retesting those operators already licensed to run nuclear power plants and, it hoped, improving the education of those who hoped to.

In addition, the NRC improved its inspection procedures, getting stricter about safety violations and levying stiffer fines when it found them. It also changed its licensing procedures, placing an increased burden on license applicants to demonstrate that proposed plants were safe and, in the process, providing the antinuclear opposition with additional avenues for delaying plant construction and licensing in the courts. The NRC's response to the accident at Three Mile Island also proved expensive for the nuclear power industry. Meeting the NRC's new demands for safety equipment is estimated to have cost the industry some $3.5 billion in capital costs, as well as some $32 billion in the costs of prolonged construction, additional interest payments, and power that had to be purchased from other sources.[15]

The major impact of the accident and its aftermath, though, was psychological. The accident gave a frightening shot in the arm to the antinuclear forces, which immediately launched a drive designed to halt further construction forever. "This is the beginning of the end," said consumer advocate Ralph Nader as NRC engineers and reporters were speeding toward southern Pennsylvania following the announcement of the March 28 accident. Others agreed and worked to make Nader's prediction a reality. Dr. Helen Caldicott, a long-time antinuclear campaigner, and Dr. Ernest Sternglass, a University of Pittsburgh researcher, visited Harrisburg and participated in news conferences at which they said that even low-level radiation, like that presumably emitted by the runaway reactor, could cause genetic damage, birth defects, and cancer.

Some environmentalists demanded the closing of all Babcock and Wilcox plants, figuring that what went wrong with the Three Mile Island plant could just as easily go wrong with other B&W facilities. Others intensified their assaults—legal and political—against plants under construction or awaiting licenses, urging that no more new plants be allowed to operate until all the recommendations of the Kemeny Commission had been implemented. Still others demonstrated, gathering outside nuclear plants from coast to coast and waving their by-now-familiar signs: HELL NO, WE WON'T GLOW. NO NUKES IS GOOD NUKES. TODAY TMI—TOMORROW . . . ?

The impact of the accident at Three Mile Island was not, however, confined to the U.S. The accident made page-one headlines in most European newspapers and received prominent play for more than a week. It also rekindled the long-smoldering nuclear debate in Germany and France. In Germany the weekly magazine *Der Spiegel* followed its coverage of the accident with a twenty-five-page special on the nuclear debate and carried an editorial calling for a rethinking of the country's nuclear policies. Unknown protesters, meanwhile, dynamited a pylon carrying transmission wires from a newly completed reactor at Esenhamm outside Hamburg. Two months after the accident in Pennsylvania, Chancellor Helmut Schmidt convened an intergovernmental conference on reactor safety. In France the conservative weekly *l'Express* ran a cover story on Three Mile Island that urged the creation of a commission to study nuclear safety and called for a parliamentary debate on the commission's findings. The government, however, had already made up its mind. Concurring with Industry Minister André Giraud's statement that for France, "It's either nuclear energy or economic recession," the government announced plans to build nine new nuclear plants over the next five years.[16]

Back in the U.S., meanwhile, Three Mile Island became the focal point for a series of debates over nuclear power. One concerned the safety of nuclear power plants in general, and found the Three Mile Island plant cast in the same role that Mark Twain once humorously assigned to the town drunk who, he said, was useful because he could always serve as a "horrible example." In New York, in California, in Michigan, antinuclear activists pointed to Three Mile Island and asked people if they wanted the same thing in their communities. Their arguments proved particularly effective in New York, where the Long Island Lighting Company was building a huge plant near the coast at Shoreham. Noting the difficulty that commuters regularly had getting from Long Island to New York and back under the best of conditions, the nuclear opponents asked locals how they thought they would be able to get off Long Island in the event of a nuclear emergency. The question proved all but unanswerable. LILCO had no workable evacuation plans. Even when it finally came up with one, most people recognized it as totally inadequate and wondered if an effective plan could ever be developed for the densely populated area around the Shoreham plant.

But power plant safety was only one issue out of many raised by the accident at Three Mile Island. Another major issue posed by the accident concerned the cost of the cleanup. From the start, officials of Metropolitan Edison and its parent, General Public Utilities, acknowledged that millions of dollars would have to be spent repairing the damage to the crippled reactor, cleaning up the mess made by the accident, and either decommissioning the plant permanently or restoring it to service. From the start, too, the utility company officials had talked of passing, if not all, then certainly the lion's share of these costs on to their customers in the form of increased rates.

Their proposal brought a rapid—and almost uniformly negative—reaction from Pennsylvania residents, who saw no reason why they should be forced to pay for what they considered the company's poor management. It brought a similar reaction from Pennsylvania Governor Richard Thornburgh, who urged that the NRC not allow Met Ed's TMI-1 unit to go back on-line until a plan for financing the cleanup had been worked out and put into effect. Thornburgh wanted the federal government and the utility industry in general to pay the major portion of the cleanup costs and thought that little—if any—of the bill should be borne by the utility's ratepayers.

Still another issue concerned low-level radiation. Scientists had known since Hiroshima that high-level radiation could produce devastating effects, from burns and radiation sickness to such cancers as leukemias and lymphomas. But scientists were not sure about the effects of low-level radiation. They pointed out that people were exposed constantly to a certain amount of naturally originating radiation—from granite buildings, from the rays of the sun, from medical, dental, and even airport X-rays—and insisted that anyone who flew on a jet plane from Pennsylvania to California would be exposed to more radiation than any member of the public was as a result of Three Mile Island.

The public, or at least a good many members of it in the area around Three Mile Island, however, rejected such reassurances. What the skeptics wanted was some believable information as to how much radiation had actually been released as a result of the accident and some credible evaluations as to what the effects of this radiation—on humans and livestock—actually were.

Still another issue concerned Three Mile Island's sister plant. Undamaged by the accident at TMI-2, TMI-1 was ready to resume generating power. Company officials wanted it to do so. They insisted that the plant's output was essential to the utility's financial health and noted that the company was buying the power from other utilities that would normally have been produced by TMI-1. They claimed, TMI-1 was essential not merely to the company's well-being, but to its very survival. Without the ability to bring Unit 1 back on-line and include it in the rate base, said officials of GPU, the company could founder, with dire consequences to the people of southern Pennsylvania.

Their arguments were unpersuasive to a great many Pennsylvanians, especially in the wake of allegations that the first of the Three Mile Island plants had also been plagued with problems and especially in the light of rumors that some of the plant's safety records had been falsified. Even though Unit 1 was fitted with millions of dollars' worth of new safety equipment after the accident at TMI-2, locals continued to object to company plans to put it back on-line. "I'm not impressed with GPU's argument that no one was hurt or killed in the accident," said a member of a Harrisburg-based anti-nuclear group. "The police don't listen to arguments like that when someone drives his car in a dangerous, reckless manner. They take away his driver's license before he does hurt or kill someone. I think we ought to do the same with GPU. I think they've shown that they are not fit to run a nuclear power plant. As far as I'm concerned, they should never be allowed to run one again."[17]

The debates continued as the cleanup commenced. GPU officials initially estimated that the cleanup would take a year or more and cost in the vicinity of $10 million. But it was not long before they began to revise both estimates upward. Special equipment had to be brought in and installed just to remove the radioactive water that had been spilled, to reduce its volume through evaporation, to solidify it by mixing it with cement, to seal it up in barrels, and to transport it to the country's only high-level nuclear waste repository, the facility at Hanford, Washington. The auxiliary building had to be scrubbed down and decontaminated. But the most difficult part of the cleanup would take even longer. NRC safety officials estimated that it might be a year or more before radiation levels dropped to the point that even a well-protected man could enter the reactor building, considerably longer before it became safe to remove the cover of the reactor itself and begin the tortuous task of extracting the damaged fuel. It would be longer still before the reactor itself could be removed, so that it could be cut up, carted away, and buried. "I wish I could tell you how long it will take to clean up this mess," said the NRC's Robert Bernero, an expert on nuclear plant decommissioning, during the summer following the accident. "But I can't. Any target date, any cost estimate I might give you would be a guess, nothing else. We simply don't know enough."

Bernero was considered unduly pessimistic when he made his statement. Time, however, proved his pessimism justified. By the autumn of 1984, engineers were making progress at TMI-2. They had decontaminated the auxiliary building and made a good start toward decontaminating the reactor building as well, washing all parts of the structure down with detergent and carrying the radioactive residues of their work away in sealed barrels. They had also managed to get the head off the reactor vessel and make a start on removing the plenum, the assembly that holds the control rods, so they could begin to assess the extent of damage to the core.

The task was a formidable one. A video camera maneuvered through a small opening in the reactor vessel revealed that almost all of the reactor's 37,000 pencil-thin fuel rods had been damaged during the accident. In fact, the top third of the reactor's core was gone, reduced to a mound of radioactive shards. But the core was in better shape than many had anticipated, suggesting that the overheating that occurred during the accident had been less severe than originally estimated.[18]

But even the completion of the "head lift" left an enormous amount of work to be done. And a long way to go before the job could be considered complete. The task, NRC and company officials estimated after the head lift, would not be completed until late 1988, more than nine years after the first red warning light began flashing in the TMI control room. But even that would not mark the end of the affair. It would only bring the company to the point where it could decide whether to attempt to restore the reactor to service or decommission it forever.

The job, all involved conceded, would also cost a great deal more than anyone had initially calculated. The cost of cleaning up TMI was estimated in late 1984 at $1 billion, only $300 million of which would be covered by insurance.[19]

Progress in the cleanup failed to resolve the question of whether GPU should reopen TMI-1. Throughout 1983 it appeared that the NRC was eager to allow the crippled reactor's sister plant to restart. Indeed, from the NRC's conduct, it had seemed that the question the commission was considering was not whether TMI-1 should restart but when. The NRC had made no secret of its lack of patience with local residents who objected to the reopening of the plant. The commission had rejected almost out of hand suggestions that it consider the psychological impact of either the 1979 accident or a decision to permit TMI-1 to go back on-line. Nor did the NRC display any eagerness to look seriously into such things as reports of widespread cheating by TMI plant operators on licensing examinations or information that leak-rate tests had been falsified.

The commission's attitude and the secrecy in which it worked deepened the distrust with which many Pennsylvanians viewed both the industry and the NRC. The commission's conduct made it some other enemies as well. The Philadelphia Newspapers, Inc., publisher of the *Philadelphia Inquirer*, sued the NRC to open its meetings to the public and won a favorable decision from the U.S. Court of Appeals. The Union of Concerned Scientists used the Freedom of Information Act to obtain documents—including transcripts of closed meetings—that the NRC would have preferred to keep private.

Excerpted and released by the UCS, the documents were disturbing. One recorded Commissioner Thomas Roberts as saying that he did not care if studies showed that the company had deliberately covered up the seriousness of the 1979 accident. "Whatever he says," said Roberts in response to a suggestion that a high-ranking NRC official be asked about his experience at the time of the accident, "and whatever transpires in no way is going to affect my decision on the restart of the plant." At other points during the proceedings, Roberts expressed concern about getting TMI-1 back on-line.

But he was not the only one to do so. The documents also showed that NRC Chairman Nunzio Palladino was eager to end what he obviously considered a drawn-out process and bring the hearings on restarting TMI-1 to a speedy and—to the company, at least—favorable conclusion.

The documents, which indicated the NRC's complete disdain for input from members of the public, input that was required both by law and, it would seem, good sense, dismayed the UCS. "Instead of government under the sunshine law, the commission provides government in dark corners," said UCS General Counsel Ellyn R. Weiss. "Until now, our work on this case has focused largely on the competence and integrity of GPU Nuclear [the new subsidiary formed by GPU to conduct the cleanup of TMI-2 and to run the undamaged plant at Three Mile Island]. Now, we are forced to question the competence and integrity of the NRC."[20]

Through the spring and summer of 1984, it appeared that nothing could prevent the NRC from allowing TMI-1 to restart. When area residents asked the NRC to look into the accident's effects on health and mortality rates in the area surrounding the plant, the NRC dismissed their request by reiterating its old claim that the amount of radiation released during the 1979 mishap was too small to have caused *any* untoward health effects.

The NRC's action, or rather, the lack thereof, did not make the claims go away. A year after the accident, many residents of Middletown, the community closest to Three Mile Island, were found to be suffering from what one local physician called "nuclear neurosis," one symptom of which was a readiness to blame anything that went on in their lives, from the common cold to cancer, on radiation released during the accident. Their apprehension was understandable. In the years immediately following the accident, pregnant women had heard experts arguing, disagreeing, and reaching no conclusions on whether a slight increase in miscarriages, infant deaths, and thyroid problems in the area might be the result of radiation exposure. The fears of area residents were further fanned by reports of bizarre happenings on nearby farms—stories of miscarriages, sudden death, and deformities among cows, sheep, and swine. In March 1980, a year after the accident, a former Pennsylvania health official revealed that he had observed a 50 percent increase in the number of infant deaths within a ten-mile radius of the reactor during the first six months following the emergency. His findings were frightening. But they were also disputed. A few days later, a state health department epidemiologist said that his studies had found "no significant changes" in infant death rates before and after the accident. In fact, he produced figures to show a drop of 13 percent in infant deaths for the six-month period after the accident as compared with the six months that preceded it.[21]

The various sets of figures did little to convince locals; those who wanted to hold the accident responsible for health problems continued to do so. One Lancaster woman kept her own tally of deaths, assuming that any case of cancer that occurred *after* the accident occurred *because* of it, and became annoyed when some of the newsmen she called with her findings told her that they were interesting but proved nothing.

Still, protesters persisted, particularly a Coatesville couple named Marjorie and Norman Aamodt. Noting that not even the NRC could say with certainty how much radiation had been released during the accident (the NRC's own report on the accident notes that certain records, covering emissions of xenon and krypton gases released up the plant's exhaust stack, the release of iodine, and the results of environmental monitoring, were either lost or incomplete), and noting further that a study being conducted by Pennsylvania's health department had not been completed, the Aamodts conducted a study of their own. Interviewing some three hundred people living on high ground to the north and west of Three Mile Island, the area toward which the winds were blowing on the day of the accident, they found several who reported experiencing similar symptoms at the time of the emergency. The people they interviewed talked of metallic smells in the air and metallic tastes in their mouths. They recalled experiencing what seemed like sunburns, some of which were sufficiently severe to blister their skins. Afterward, they told their interviewers, they experienced a variety of health problems, including hair and weight loss, diarrhea and respiratory disorders, tumors, heart problems.

The Aamodts took these stories down carefully and presented them to the NRC in a series of signed affidavits. The documents did not make for reassuring reading. One man, for example, recalled that he and his son had spent Thursday, March 29, the day after the accident, working in their garage with the doors open. "That night when I took a shower," said the man, "my face, neck, and hands looked as if I was at the seashore and had gotten burned real bad. I felt nauseous. My eyes were red and burning." Like several others in the area, the man had taken his family and fled what he feared might be dangerous levels of radiation. Upon his return to his home a week later, he told the Aamodts, he found his dog and several cats dead, their eyes a "milky white." Since then, he said, he had experienced hair loss, had sores that would not heal, and heart trouble, some of which was serious enough to require the replacement of an aortic valve.

Others told similar stories of mysterious skin burning. James Gunckel, a Rutgers University botanist who had spent more than thirty years studying the effects of radiation on plants, reported that he had examined plants from the area surveyed by the Aamodts and had found changes—including extra buds and stem tumors—consistent with those induced by radiation. The Aamodts also reported that they had found slightly elevated levels of radiation, both alpha and gamma, in soil and, in one case, on a home in the area.[22]

The Aamodts' findings apparently made some impression on the NRC—as did the arguments advanced in mid-August by Governor Thornburgh. The governor appeared before the NRC, which had been expected to approve GPU's plans to restart TMI-1, and urged the commissioners to delay a start-up vote until funding for the $1 billion cleanup of Unit 2 had been assured and until all NRC hearings on the competence and integrity of the plant's operator were complete. Later that month NRC staffers called the Aamodts and asked them to direct them to the places where they had found raised radiation levels.

Even after its inspection, the NRC stuck with its earlier insistence that radiation releases from Three Mile Island had been insignificant. But, pressured by a federal court to hold hearings on Three Mile Island's operators, the commission did decide to delay a decision on restarting Unit 1 until early 1985.

The commission's decision pleased those opposed to restarting TMI-1. But it did not satisfy them, for they knew that the commission had merely delayed a decision that all expected would eventually be made in the utility's favor.

Nor did the NRC's decision restore the public's badly shaken faith in the ability of the agency to regulate nuclear power and protect people from its hazards. Antinuclear activists, both in Pennsylvania and elsewhere, in fact, saw the NRC's action as nothing more than additional evidence to support their oft-made claim that the commission would never do any more than it was forced to do and that it still considered itself the industry's protector rather than its policeman. "Nothing the NRC has done since the accident at Three Mile Island has given me any reassurance that things like this won't happen again," said the UCS's Weiss.[23] Her statement, endorsed by other antinuclear activists, gave the NRC a good idea of where it stood five years after the country's worst nuclear plant accident and showed the NRC how little it had done to restore public confidence in either itself or the industry it oversaw. The message to the NRC was clear. Unfortunately, the NRC chose not to heed it.

Eight

Storm Warnings

"Russians," quipped France's legendary Madame de Staël, "never achieve their objectives. They always go past them." So, apparently, do Californians, at least those Californians concerned with building and operating nuclear power plants. Anyone in the power business can make one mistake. Almost anyone, it seems, can make two or even three. But few, it seems, can make as many mistakes as the giant California utility Pacific Gas and Electric Company did when it came to building the Diablo Canyon Nuclear Power Plant. For a while it looked as though the company was trying to establish some sort of record.

Diablo Canyon, located in San Luis Obispo on a stretch of wooded shoreline midway between Los Angeles and San Francisco, made some sense when it was first conceived in the midsixties. The plant's two Westinghouse pressurized water reactors were to have a capacity of 2,000 megawatts, enough to serve a residential population of 1.7 million. And the capacity looked as if it would be needed. Demand for electricity had been rising steadily as the nation's economy expanded. California's population had been increasing rapidly as restless Americans, seeking sun and a more laid-back lifestyle, trekked west and settled in the state.

At the time it was started, the plant did not seem unduly expensive. When construction began in 1969, the projected cost for the

134

facility was $350 million. Nor was the plant expected to take an inordinately long time to complete. When PG&E first obtained construction permits in 1968, it expected that the plant would begin operating in 1973. It did not radically revise its prediction when work actually started. In 1969 PG&E officials still expected that the plant would be on-line and producing electricity by 1975.[1]

But it was not long before PG&E encountered its first problems with the plant. Knowing of California's history of earthquakes, engineers had designed Diablo Canyon to withstand a shock measuring 6.5 on the open-ended Richter scale. They had calculated that 6.5 was the biggest shock likely to occur in the area surrounding the plant. But by 1971 these calculations came under question. The cause of the question was a report by two oil geologists who revealed that they had discovered a major earthquake fault only two and a half miles out into the ocean from the nuclear plant site.

The United States Geological Survey confirmed the geologists' discovery—and added some disturbing findings of its own. The USGS said that the crack, known as the Hosgri Fault, was capable of producing a shock that would measure 7.5 on the Richter scale.

The USGS finding was frightening. The Richter scale measures earthquake intensity exponentially, which means that its numbers increase by a factor of ten. This means that a 7.5 shock is not just slightly stronger than one measuring 6.5; a shock measuring 7.5 is, it turns out, ten times as powerful as one that measures 6.5.[2]

Environmentalists, who had opposed the plant on aesthetic and safety grounds, were galvanized into action by the report that the plant sat dangerously close to a major earthquake fault. They followed the publication of the report with protests to the AEC, arguing that work on the plant should be halted and that no other plants should be allowed to be built anywhere near earthquake faults, a proposal that, had it been granted, would have effectively precluded any nuclear plant construction in earthquake-prone California. Their protests proved at least partially effective. In 1974 the AEC opened a series of hearings, which its successor, the NRC, continued. And continued. The hearings went on for five years. They involved 339 witnesses. They produced 10,812 pages of testimony. They forced PG&E to spend close to $3 billion in structural alterations and reinforcement in order to make the plant capable of withstanding a 7.5 quake. But they did not satisfy the plant's opponents. They dismissed PG&E's changes as "cosmetic mathematics" and insisted that Diablo Canyon was still unsafe.[3]

The NRC, however, felt that it was. On September 27, 1979, the commission's licensing board issued a finding that the plant could withstand any earthquake likely to occur in the area. The timing of its decision proved ironic. Less than three weeks after it was released, California was shaken by an earthquake. Known as the Imperial Valley quake and centered down near the Mexican border, some 350 miles south of the plant site at San Luis Obispo, the quake was nowhere near as big as the 8.3 catastrophe that destroyed San Francisco. But at 6.4, it was big enough, big enough certainly to damage some structures that had previously been considered earthquake-proof and impressive enough to raise questions about the destructive potential of the intricate network of earthquake faults that extends for most of the length of California. It was big enough, too, to force the NRC to reopen its hearings on the safety of the Diablo Canyon plant.[4]

And not merely as far as earthquakes were concerned. Prodded by three regional organizations—Mothers for Peace, the Scenic Shoreline Preservation Conference, and the Ecology Action Club—as well as by unaffiliated residents of San Luis Obispo, the NRC ordered its hearing board to consider two other issues. One was the question of whether the plant's security arrangements were sufficient to protect it from sabotage. The other was the question of whether PG&E and local officials had made adequate arrangements to guarantee the public's safety—including plans for evacuating the area—in case of an emergency like the one that occurred in 1979 at Pennsylvania's Three Mile Island.

The opposition, of course, charged that PG&E had not dealt adequately with either of these two issues. But the environmental groups were not the only ones trying to block, first, construction, then, the actual opening and operation of Diablo Canyon. Another of the plant's opponents was Governor Edmund G. "Jerry" Brown, Jr., the unconventional chief executive of the state and a long-time opponent of nuclear power. In December 1979, Brown filed an eight-page brief challenging the NRC findings on earthquake safety and joining formally in the proceedings against Diablo Canyon as a participant.

The opposition proved expensive. The challenges stretched out the time necessary to carry out construction, and in the process, increased the cost of the plant. In 1980, with construction at least five years behind schedule, PG&E officials admitted that they were paying $14 million a month in interest on the $1.9 billion in capital tied up in Diablo Canyon. They also admitted that, considering both inflation and rising interest rates, the cost of the plant was increasing at the rate of $20,000 an hour.

And these figures failed to take into account the other expense caused by the delay. Though PG&E officials declined to release any data, outside observers estimated that the company was spending several million dollars a year to replace the power that Diablo Canyon was not generating by buying it from other sources.[5]

Nineteen-eighty was a bad year for PG&E. But 1981 proved worse. For in the late summer of that year, opponents began assembling for what they hoped would be the biggest antinuclear demonstration ever held. It was organized by the Abalone Alliance, which took its name from a 1974 test of Diablo Canyon's cooling system that killed thousands of the prized mollusks, and its tactics from the Clamshell Alliance that had demonstrated so dramatically at New Hampshire's Seabrook nuclear station. The demonstration was supposed to blockade the plant, stop workers and equipment from getting in and out, and prevent plant workers from loading the fuel necessary for the low-power testing of the reactor that the NRC was expected to allow early in September. Planned like a military maneuver, the demonstration was nothing if not ambitious. The Abalone Alliance planned to blockade the four gates that gave access to the plant. The alliance also planned other actions to keep the plant from operating. Landing parties were organized to approach the plant from its seaward side. Swimmers were recruited to tread water near the plant's four giant intake pipes, in effect daring the plant's operators to start up the reactor. The demonstrators were not sure that they could shut down Diablo Canyon. But they hoped, as organizer Pam Metcalf told *The Wall Street Journal,* to attract a good deal of attention so that "people around the world will be heartened and fight nuclear power."[6]

The antinuclear forces, though, were not the only ones to make plans. Remembering the Seabrook fiasco, PG&E and local officials also made some preparations. Questioning whether the Abalone Alliance could control the 5,000 to 10,000 demonstrators it anticipated attracting, San Luis Obispo County Sheriff George Whiting called up reinforcements and told them to be prepared for violence. PG&E also made it clear that it was ready if the protesters wanted to play rough. The company constructed a target range a short distance from the reactors and let it be known that uniformed guards were practicing their marksmanship in case it became necessary for them to shoot to prevent sabotage or theft of nuclear fuel. Company officials also put out word that the area within Diablo Canyon's security fence was guarded by dogs and, to further discourage demonstrators, also reported that the plant site was infested with rattlesnakes. Just in case, the company moved trailers onto the site to house plant workers and readied helicopters in case it proved necessary to fly food into the besieged site. Even Governor Brown, who opposed the plant, made it clear that lawlessness would not be tolerated. He sent some 500 California Highway Patrol officers into the area to back up local police and sheriff's deputies and promised to send the National Guard if the police proved too few to handle the demonstrators.

Through late August, both sides readied themselves for the confrontation. In mid-September, as the NRC voted unanimously to allow PG&E to start low-power testing at the first of Diablo Canyon's two reactors, a force of some 2,500 protesters, most, though not all, of them young, flooded into San Luis Obispo, a town of 35,000, and descended on the plant site.

The Abalone Alliance, which had hoped to attract at least twice that number, was disappointed, conceding that its strategy for blockading the plant simply was not ready. Still, the protesters made up in enthusiasm and determination what they lacked in numbers. Though the 250 protesters who converged on the plant's main gate were outnumbered by newsmen and able to do little more than chant slogans and wave signs, others proved a bit more effective. Some 25 demonstrators did manage to reach PG&E's beachfront by rubber raft, and a small group, carrying specially made ladders, did manage to scale the fence and occupy a piece of ground inside the plant site, where they sat down and sang songs.

The protest, like a siege, continued for nearly two weeks, with some demonstrators leaving, others joining—and many being arrested. When it was over, both sides claimed victory. The Abalone Alliance noted with some pride that the protest resulted in nearly 1,900 arrests, more than any other antinuclear demonstration in U.S. history. "We feel it was a really strong, really positive action," said Steven Leeds, an Abalone Alliance spokesman. "We elevated the issue of nuclear power and Diablo Canyon and nuclear weaponry one step up."[7]

But in terms of accomplishing its stated objective, the demonstration was a failure. It did not prevent PG&E from testing at least one of the reactors at the twin-domed $2.3 billion nuclear power plant.

It did not, in fact, cause the company more than a moderate amount of inconvenience. "To sum it up succinctly," said PG&E spokesman Gregg Pruett after the action was over, "they had absolutely no effect."[8]

There is no question that PG&E survived the siege of Diablo Canyon. But protesters were not the only problem plaguing the plant. Before the year was over, the company had a more serious problem. A few days after the NRC had awarded Diablo Canyon a start-up license, engineers at the utility discovered that someone had made a serious mistake. Someone, they found, had mixed up the blueprints for earthquake structures on Unit 1, which was thought to be finished, and Unit 2, which was still under construction. The discovery that incorrect blueprints were used to construct pipe hangers placed PG&E in a difficult position, as company officials themselves were quick to concede. It meant that the hangers might not have been adequate to withstand a 7.5 earthquake as required.[9]

To its credit, PG&E moved quickly to reexamine the plant, ordering an extensive study of pipes, valves, electrical conduits, and mechanical equipment. "We have to conduct the tests," a company spokesman said. "We can't just look at the hangers and ignore the electrical conduits and mechanical equipment that are tied to them."

To its even greater credit, the NRC got into the act. Deciding that only some sort of public spanking would serve to signal the nuclear industry that sloppy work would not be tolerated, the commission voted in November to suspend Diablo Canyon's start-up license and to forbid PG&E to load fuel into the plant pending a review of its safeguards against earthquake damage. Said NRC Chairman Nunzio Palladino of the commission's action: "This sends a strong signal that the commission doesn't like what it is seeing in this case."[10]

The signal was strong, indeed. PG&E had declared that it would not use the license—granted only two months earlier—to load fuel and conduct tests of the reactor at 5 percent of full power until it had straightened out all earthquake-related problems in the plant's design and structure. The NRC decision went farther, saying that the utility *could not* conduct such tests. The NRC also ordered an outside firm to conduct a full audit of quality-control procedures at Diablo Canyon.

The NRC had good reason for this last action. The utility had already engaged an "independent" auditor to review its calculations on safety. But his review turned out to be somewhat less than independent. The NRC had learned that the auditor had sent a draft of his report to the utility a few weeks before he sent the commission a favorable report on PG&E.[11]

The result of all these delays was that it was not until 1984 that Diablo Canyon began to produce any electricity. And even then, its start-up was marred by an accident. In April, nearly ten years behind schedule, the operators at the plant finally withdrew the control rods from Unit 1's core. A few minutes later the plant began to produce electricity. But a few hours after that, the plant sprang a leak. According to plant officials, the leak developed when a three-way valve in one of the facility's coolant systems opened, allowing what they called "a slight redirection of water." The leak, which was brought under control in about ten minutes, was nowhere near as serious as the leak that had occurred five years earlier at Three Mile Island. The cooling system lost less than two gallons a minute, and the water, given the fact that the reactor had barely begun operating, was barely radioactive.[12]

But the leak did give opponents of PG&E's newest nuclear plant, some eighty of whom gathered outside the gate to protest its start-up, further ammunition for their continuing barrage against the installation. And it did nothing to still the storm of controversy that continued to swirl around Diablo Canyon, the cost of which had risen to $4.9 billion. Environmentalists continued to insist that the plant was essentially unsafe, despite the assurances of both the company and the NRC that Diablo Canyon was capable of withstanding any earthquake that might rattle it. Most agreed with the Abalone Alliance's Pam Metcalf when she said, "Now that they are starting the process of nuclear fission, the prospect of a Three Mile Island type of accident is something we have to live with day after day."[13]

Opponents were also worried by allegations by former plant engineers and workers, some of whom claimed that they had been dismissed for raising questions about plant safety. Charles Stokes, an engineer who had worked as a plant inspector prior to his dismissal, told the NRC that he had found PG&E using improper and outdated specifications for construction and accepting work that had previously been judged inadequate. Steven Lockert, who had worked as a welding inspector for one of the plant's subcontractors, charged that the firm used unqualified welders. They both painted a gloomy picture of the plant's ability to survive the strains of full-scale operation. "It may take twenty years, but I feel that it's a certainty that we'll have a major leak of radiation or a meltdown," Stokes told *The*

New York Times in an interview. Lockert made a similar prediction. "As they go through low-power testing, the things that are wrong with the plant will become apparent," he said. "I don't think they will get very far."

Their warnings carried little weight with PG&E, which dismissed them as the laments of those who had lost a fight. Nor did they impress the NRC, which said that it saw "no apparent risk to the public health and safety" in the plant's operations at reduced power.[14]

The environmentalists' arguments did, however, eventually carry some weight with the federal courts. As 1984 wore on, PG&E began to get impatient about opening its plant and recouping some of the investment, now up to $5.1 billion, that it had made to get it built. In August the NRC granted the company a license to begin commercial operation of one of the plant's two reactors. But a week later, a three-judge panel of the U.S. District Court of Appeals, heeding pleas from plant opponents, blocked the license pending the completion of a full hearing on evacuation plans and earthquake safety at the Diablo Canyon site.

PG&E responded by appealing the panel's ruling, asking the full court to overturn the decision halting its operation. Tactically, the move proved to be a mistake. Early in October the entire twelve-member court, without offering any explanation for its action, declined to review the earlier rulings, effectively upholding the decision by the three-judge panel and just as effectively preventing PG&E from putting its costly plant into operation.

Company officials were predictably disappointed by the decision, which seemed to foreclose any move to start up the plant or to generate electricity before the completion of hearings that were not even expected to begin before early 1985. But opponents of Diablo Canyon were elated. "This just about exhausts the avenues that PG&E has available to it for overturning the court's stay," said Joel Reynolds, the attorney for the opponents.[15]

The decision placed PG&E in a bind, saddling it with an expensive plant that it could not figure into its rate base. It also pointed up a problem that had plagued the nuclear power industry for years—an inability to built plants economically.

The problem was a serious one. It had been years since utility executives and others had dismissed the prediction of one-time AEC Chairman Lewis Strauss that electricity from the atom would be "too cheap to meter." Everyone, from the NRC on down, knew that nuclear power was not and had never been that inexpensive. But in the face of mounting evidence to the contrary, a great many people who should have known better continued to calculate and insist that nuclear power was cheaper than that provided by burning coal.

One of those who persisted in this belief was the Atomic Industrial Forum. In 1979, the AIF issued a report saying that the costs of generating electricity from nuclear plants were lower than those of generating electricity from coal. Read quickly, the AIF claim was impressive. It said that the costs of generating electricity from nuclear power had remained stable in 1978, holding at that level for the third year in a row while the costs of coal- and oil-produced electricity rose. According to the AIF, the average cost per kilowatt hour of nuclear-produced electricity was 1.5 cents, the same as it had been in 1976 and 1977. But, said the AIF, coal-generated electricity cost 2.3 cents a kilowatt hour, up from 2.0 cents in 1977 and 1.8 cents in 1976. Oil was even more expensive at 4.0 cents a kilowatt hour.[16]

The AIF described its findings as evidence that Three Mile Island had not made nuclear power either unnecessary or undesirable. "Nuclear energy's excellent performance as a source of electricity in this and many other countries should not go unnoticed because of the well-publicized difficulties experienced by the nuclear industry this year," said AIF President Carl Walske.

Critics, however, characterized the AIF findings as "hogwash," and one, a New York–based independent energy consultant named Charles Komanoff, quietly, gleefully, and rather effectively took them apart. In a report prepared for the Washington-based Environmental Action Foundation, Komanoff charged the AIF with relying upon "a distorted data base," and called its conclusions "misleading to the point of falsehood." He then backed up his criticism with a detailed analysis of the AIF study, showing, among other things, that the organization had based its studies on information about fewer than two-thirds of U.S. commercial power reactors rather than the nine-tenths figure its release implied. Komanoff also noted that the AIF had eliminated from its study the plants with the highest construction costs and the worst performance records; the twenty-one reactors omitted from the study, he charged, had not only cost an average of 60 percent more than other reactors to construct, but produced 19 percent less electricity. Furthermore, Komanoff alleged, the AIF survey had failed to make sufficient allowance for the costs of disposing of nuclear wastes and decommissioning aged installations, both of which must eventually be paid by utility customers. In addition, he said, the study excluded lower-cost coal plants operated by the country's two largest utilities, the TVA and American Electric Power, and penalized other coal-fired plants for being below their potential due to the industry's excess generating capacity. "These," said Komanoff of the AIF's claims, "are some of the most misleading statements I have ever seen."[17]

To correct them, Komanoff presented some data of his own. Factoring in the twenty-one reactors eliminated from the study and inserting their average generating cost of 2.62 cents per kilowatt hour into the equation, adding in the 1.5 cents per kilowatt hour cost of disposing of nuclear waste and decommissioning plants, making other adjustments to remove the arbitrary penalties imposed on certain coal plants and including the lower cost of electricity generated by TVA and American Electric coal plants gave Komanoff a different set of figures. Based on them, he added 0.50 cents per kilowatt hour to the cost of generating electricity by means of the atom, subtracted 0.42 cents from the cost of generating power by burning coal.

The results of Komanoff's new calculations gave coal a decided advantage where cost was concerned. According to his findings, coal plants could generate electricity for 1.9 cents a kilowatt hour. Nuclear plants could not produce power for less than 2.04 cents a kilowatt hour.[18]

A year later, Komanoff struck again. Working with Alden Meyer of the Environmental Action Foundation, Komanoff went over the AIF's 1981 report and concluded that the new survey contained "many of the same flaws and biases that have so damaged the credibility of earlier AIF surveys." But despite this problem, the pair noted, the AIF survey itself provided "clear evidence" that nuclear power's economic position was rapidly deteriorating. The reason was that for the first time, the AIF had broken its coal and nuclear cost estimates down according to the years in which the plants surveyed began commercial operation. The organization's own figures thus showed that while the older, original nuclear power plants could compete with coal plants where costs were concerned, the plants built since the middle of the seventies could not. Looking at coal and nuclear plants built since 1975, said Komanoff, it was clear that coal offered an economic advantage over the atom. For reactors entering service between 1970 and 1974, AIF figures pointed to a 1979 generating cost of 1.60 cents per kilowatt hour. But reactors that came on-line between 1975 and 1978 could not generate electricity for less than 2.73 cents a kilowatt hour. In contrast, the coal units that came on-line between 1975 and 1978 were able in 1979 to generate electricity for 2.35 cents a kilowatt hour, 14 percent less than comparable nuclear plants. "It is ironic," said Meyer, "that a survey designed by nuclear boosters to convince the media and the public of nuclear power's economic advantages demonstrates that, on the contrary, nuclear electricity has become far more costly than power from coal." [19]

According to Komanoff, the AIF continued to employ several practices that tended to understate the costs of nuclear power while overstating those of coal power. One of the things the AIF did was omit from its survey several particularly expensive reactors, including Three Mile Island's Unit 2, whose inclusion would have raised the average cost of nuclear electricity by at least a tenth of a cent per kilowatt hour. Another thing the AIF did was omit the cost of decommissioning nuclear plants or disposing of their wastes, expenses that, had they been conservatively estimated and included, would have raised the costs of nuclear power another two-tenths of a cent. Finally, charged Komanoff, the AIF selected its coal sample in such a way as to penalize those coal-fired units that operated below capacity because of insufficient demand.

Eliminating these "errors," Komanoff did his own calculations. He said: "When these errors are corrected, the average coal cost for the plants included in the AIF survey is reduced to 2.14 cents per kilowatt hour and the overall average nuclear cost increases to 2.32 cents." More significantly, Komanoff found, for plants installed after 1974, the corrected coal average was 2.26 cents per kilowatt hour, while the corrected nuclear average climbed to 3.16 cents per kilowatt hour, or 40 percent more than coal.

Komanoff's calculations did not help the nuclear power industry, which was already struggling to convince potential customers that nuclear power was a bargain. The industry had been dealt a blow in 1978, when a congressional Committee on Governmental Operations released a report knocking nuclear power's advantages. "Contrary to widespread belief," said the report, "nuclear power is no longer a cheap energy source. In fact, when the still unknown costs of radioactive waste and spent fuel management, decommissioning and perpetual care are finally included in the rate base, nuclear power may prove to be much more expensive than conventional energy sources such as coal and oil and may well not be economically competitive with safe, renewable resource energy alternatives such as solar power." [20]

Komanoff dealt the industry another blow when he predicted that the atom would continue to lose whatever advantages it might once have possessed. In a comprehensive study of power plant cost escalation during the decade of the seventies, he forecast that nuclear costs would continue to go up faster than those of coal. Komanoff began his study from the finding that nuclear and coal costs had been roughly equivalent in 1978. Then, assuming a continuous 7 percent inflation rate, he figured the capital costs of nuclear plants coming on-line in the late eighties would average $2,500 a kilowatt—far more than the $1,250 per kilowatt average for small, efficient coal plants, including those equipped with state-of-the-art antipollution equipment. He also calculated that coal plants would be cheaper to operate. He figured the generating costs of the coming generation of nuclear plants at 11.0 cents per kilowatt hour. He calculated the generating costs for coal plants at 7.0 cents a kilowatt hour. The nuclear and coal cost trends, Komanoff said, would continue to favor coal. Early in 1984, in fact, Komanoff released a new set of figures, derived from projecting the costs in constant, 1979 dollars, of electricity from power plants completed in 1988. He predicted that electricity from coal plants equipped with "scrubbers" to eliminate the most noxious of their emissions would cost 3.9 cents a kilowatt hour, while electricity from nuclear plants would cost 4.8 cents, or slightly over 25 percent more.[21]

As Komanoff and others noted, the mere mechanics of power plant construction tend to give coal an economic edge. Two-thirds of the price of nuclear electricity represents capital costs, one-third operating expenses such as fuel. With coal, the proportions are reversed. The price of coal-generated electricity is only one-third capital cost.

The difference is dramatic. According to Komanoff, the capital costs of nuclear plants increased at a rate three times that of the general inflation rate during the seventies. Nuclear plant costs also increased at a rate one and a half times that of coal-fired plants. In 1972, for example, the costs of building nuclear and coal plants were about the same; nuclear plants cost $146 a kilowatt to build, coal plants $145. By 1978, though, the distance had doubled. Coal plants cost $377 a kilowatt without scrubbers, $483 a kilowatt with them. But nuclear power plants cost $718 a kilowatt.[22]

The reasons for the rise were anything but obscure. The NRC's gradually increasing emphasis on safety added enormously to the cost of building a nuclear power plant. Opposition from environmentalists and other antinuclear groups added to the time it took to bring a plant from the planning stage to the point where it could begin to produce power. Taking advantage of the laws and exploiting the opportunities provided by the NRC's hearing procedures, antinuclear forces tied would-be nuclear plant builders and operators up in the courts, turning what had once been a fairly brief construction job into something that utility executives compared to building the Pyramids. In the sixties, it took an average of four to six years to get a nuclear plant off the drawing board and into the power grid. By the late seventies, the construction time had stretched to twelve to fifteen years. Indeed, a study by the International Consultative Group on Nuclear Energy calculated that delays due to siting and regulatory problems had added from three and a half to seven years to the interval between "project definition," or the decision to build, and commercial operation. The impact of the extension was demoralizing, for it meant that nuclear power plant construction lead times exceeded the utility industry's normal ten-year planning horizons.[23]

The extension also proved expensive, for it meant that utilities could never tell in advance just how long a nuclear plant would take to build. And this, in turn, meant that utilities could not figure out in advance what a particular power plant would cost either. All they could know for certain at the start of a project was that it would cost more than they figured. The delays meant that utilities that wanted to build nuclear power plants had to tie up enormous amounts of money and pay enormous amounts of interest on it before they could even dream of recouping their investments.

The equation was simple: lengthening lead times equaled spiraling capital costs. A study completed by the Electric Power Research Institute in 1975 calculated that a 1,200-megawatt plant that might cost $1.075 billion if built in six years would cost $1.6 billion, or $525 million more, if it was built in ten years. Of the increased cost, said the study, $265 million represented the extra interest the company would have to pay during construction, assuming an overoptimistically low interest rate of 12 percent. The other $260 million represented cost escalation, again assuming an inflation rate of 12 percent.[24]

"We can't go on like this," said one utility executive of the situation. "If we do, we're going to build ourselves into bankruptcy."

Other utility executives agreed and sought relief—from the regulations they felt were stifling their industry's development, from the environmentalists they felt were harassing them, from the public they felt failed to appreciate them. President Ronald Reagan attempted to provide this relief. During his campaign for the White House, he had pledged to reduce governmental interference in both the affairs of corporations and the lives of individuals and, among other things, to push for the continued development of nuclear power as a way of reducing U.S. dependence on imported sources of energy. Shortly after taking office, he acted on his promise and formally announced the steps that his administration would take to revive commercial nuclear power. Most of them involved removing regulations. "The federal government has created a regulatory environment that is forcing many utilities to rule out nuclear power as a source of new generating capacity," the President said. "Nuclear power has become entangled in a morass of regulations that do not enhance safety but that do cause extensive licensing delays and economic uncertainty."[25]

To remedy the problem, the President took several steps. He directed Energy Secretary James Edwards to give high priority to recommending ways of speeding the regulatory and licensing processes for new plants so that the twelve-to-fifteen-year period required to build them could be brought back to a more reasonable six to eight years. He confirmed the government's intention to move swiftly on creating a permanent repository for the disposal of high-level nuclear wastes. He lifted the ban President Carter had imposed in 1977 on the reprocessing of spent nuclear fuel, a measure the President had taken in response to fears that plutonium extracted from spent fuel would add to the problems involved in controlling the proliferation of nuclear weapons. He asked for a study of the feasibility of obtaining plutonium for weapons through competitive procurement instead of relying solely on government-owned facilities.

The President's proposals did, in fact, address a number of the problems plaguing the nuclear power industry. Industry advocates had only to remember the ten years it had taken for Pacific Gas and Electric to get preliminary approval to operate its Diablo Canyon plant to appreciate the President's proposal to cut nuclear plant construction time. Even the public could appreciate his announcement that the government would find a place where it could permanently store high-level wastes. In the absence of such a site, nuclear wastes had been accumulating at nuclear plants, where they were stored in water-filled "swimming pools" that were gradually becoming filled.

The industry was understandably encouraged by the President's proposals. George Gleason of the American Nuclear Energy Council said that they showed that the administration had recognized many of the problems facing the industry. But antinuclear forces opposed them. Betsy Taylor of the Nuclear Information and Resources Service called the plan "a get-well card from the president," and said that it would not revive an industry that was plagued with "real safety and economic problems." Richard Ottinger, a New York Democrat who chaired the House Energy and Commerce Committee's Subcommittee on Energy Conservation and Power, said that the President's proposals amounted to "nothing more than a Chrysler-type bailout that will cost taxpayers billions of dollars."[26]

There is no question that the Presidential program contained a few plums for the nuclear power industry. The biggest of these was the Clinch River Breeder Reactor Program, a project designed to build a large breeder reactor. The President's endorsement of the idea was bound to be controversial. When first approved by Congress in 1972, the CRBRP was seen as a symbol of the nation's commitment to nuclear power. The goal of the program was to build a 380-megawatt, liquid-metal-cooled breeder that would demonstrate the feasibility of breeder reactors in general and serve as a model for the eventual development of large, 1,000-megawatt commercial breeder reactors.[27]

For a country that thought it was going nuclear in a big way, the idea of the breeder, a reactor that would convert U-238 into highly fissile plutonium and thus produce more fuel than it consumed, made sense. It assured that there would always be plentiful supplies of nuclear fuel. But for a country worried about the proliferation of nuclear weapons, breeders posed a problem, for the plutonium they produced could easily be converted into the stuff of bombs, and an abundance of it would assure a plentiful supply of weapons-grade material for those interested in increasing their arsenals.

The organization of the program also posed problems. The CRBRP was supposed to be a joint venture between government and private industry. But to the dismay of those who questioned the need for the program at all, the government seemed to be carrying the greatest burden. By 1979, with the project already five years behind schedule and not expected to be completed by 1983, its projected cost had climbed to $1.9 billion. Industry had committed itself to provide $260 million of that amount. But by 1979 it had chipped in only $100 million and run into problems coming up with the balance.

The CRBRP had some solid support in Congress, particularly that of Senate Minority Leader Howard Baker, in whose state of Tennessee it was located. But it had some ardent opponents, too, and not just among those who opposed nuclear power in general or worried about the breeder's part in the proliferation problem in particular. Many engineers and technical experts maintained that even if the project was completed, the Clinch River breeder was of such an old design that it would be obsolete before it could be operated. Others argued that it was too small to provide a meaningful demonstration of the breeder's commercial viability. Still others looked askance at the project's financing, wondering why, if the breeder was such a good idea, industry was not willing to contribute more to the cost of its development. "It looks like the early sixties all over again," said one critic. "Industry wants the government to take all the risks, bear all the costs of developing a technology, then adopt it if it works."

It was not long before opponents of the program began to make themselves heard in Congress. By the early eighties, senators and representatives in both parties were coming to regard Clinch River as an expensive boondoggle and to resist administration requests for continued funding of the program.

The President's endorsement of CRBRP helped proponents to stave off a 1983 attempt to cut its funding. But by mid-1983 it was clear that Clinch River was in serious trouble, and that, in an era characterized by assiduous attempts to reduce domestic spending, Congress was finding it harder and harder to keep the program alive. The program suffered a serious blow when Senator Baker announced that he would not seek reelection, further eroding the Energy Department's prospects of keeping the work going for another year. A report by the Government Accounting Office had already suggested that the government would lose no more financially by killing CRBRP than it would have to spend to keep it going.[28] A number of influential congressmen suggested that industry would best show its faith in breeder technology by taking over the project itself. By early spring 1984, it was clear that Clinch River's days were numbered and that the chances for congressional approval of the President's $270 million budget request for CRBRP were fading. In June, the axe fell. The House overwhelmingly passed an energy appropriations bill containing no money, not a penny, for CRBRP. Two weeks later, the Senate concurred. The failure of the funding measure did not kill CRBRP outright; there was enough money in the pipeline to permit at least some work on the project, for which a site had been cleared near Oak Ridge, to go forward, although at a greatly reduced speed. Backers talked of reviving the program. Opponents, knowing of Clinch River's uncanny ability to survive, waited to see what form a new version of the project would take. But no one expected to know for several years. Barring a dramatic change in both public attitudes and government financial problems, though, Clinch River seemed likely to stay in a state of suspended animation.

The nuclear industry was upset by the apparent collapse of the CRBRP. But it was encouraged by President Reagan's advocacy of nuclear power and pleased by his promise that things would get better. A few utilities, realizing that the nuclear plants they had ordered in the early seventies could prove both expensive and unnecessary, canceled their orders and put their plans to build new nuclear plants on hold. A few saw the signs that the economy was slowing and decided at least to wait and see what might happen. Their decision was wise, for the signs of a slowdown in early 1984 were unmistakable. Energy consumption in the U.S. had risen rapidly in the years following World War II and the Korean conflict. Energy consumption had climbed by a third between 1960 and 1970. But the rate of increase had slowed significantly following the oil shocks of the seventies and actually dropped during the last years of the decade. A study undertaken by the AEC in 1974 to justify the breeder program had estimated that Americans would consume a total of 94 quadrillion BTUs (or "quads") of energy in 1980, and use 10.2 quads of electricity. Those in the power industry could see how far off this prediction had been by the end of that year, when final figures showed that Americans had consumed only 76 quads of energy and only 7.4 quads of electricity.[29]

But many ignored such indicators and continued to push ahead with their plans to build nuclear plants. The AEC, after all, had predicted that uranium would provide half of all American electric power by the year 2000, so many utilities turned their backs on the obvious warnings and tried to deny—or forget—the fact that nuclear plants ordered in the seventies were coming on-line at double and triple their originally projected prices. No utilities ordered new nuclear plants in the eighties, but many pressed ahead with plants under construction despite the fact that they already had more generating capacity than they needed or than they were likely to need in the foreseeable future. Some did it out of pure pride, convinced that canceling a plant was tantamount to surrendering to the hated environmentalists and antinuclear activists. Some continued because they could not bring themselves to cancel installations into which they had already poured billions. They felt that their only hope of recovering their investments lay in finishing the plants and getting them on-line and into their rate bases. Some continued because they were convinced that the economic recovery that began in mid-1984 would not only continue but accelerate. But at least a few wondered if they were doing the right thing. "Sometimes I feel as if I'm the cruise director of the *Titanic*," said a top official of a major midwestern utility, "trying to organize deck games while the ship is going down."

Others may have shared his feeling but felt themselves unable to express it. To their credit, at least a few looked at their industry, saw a house of cards, and asked themselves when it would collapse.

The answer to their question came sooner than they expected.

Nine

The Crash of '84

It was one of the most ambitious nuclear power programs ever undertaken. It turned out to be one of the biggest financial disasters the industry—and the U.S.—ever experienced. It aimed at providing inexpensive electric power for millions of customers. It ended up costing millions of investors billions of dollars. It was intended to demonstrate how small utilities could jointly launch and manage projects too large for any of them to take on individually. It ended up by providing the nuclear power and utility industries, the financial community, and nuclear critics with an almost classical example of bad planning and incompetent management. It was called "Whoops."

The origins of the debacle known as Whoops go back to 1957 when nineteen Pacific Northwest public utility districts and four Washington cities got together and formed an entity called the Washington Public Power Supply System, or WPPSS. The consortium's original purpose was to provide a framework within which companies could share power and assure their customers a plentiful supply of electricity. Back in the early seventies, it appeared that the steadily rising demand for electricity would outrun the supply, and soon, so WPPSS agreed to a plan drawn up by the federal Bonneville Power Administration, operator of the Bonneville Dam, and northwest utilities, to build three nuclear power plants.[1]

152

The utilities, none of them particularly large, got some valuable assistance when it came to financing the project, which they decided to do by taking advantage of their status and issuing tax-free bonds. Though the BPA could not, by law, own any power plants, the agency and its financial advisers devised a "net billing" scheme that enabled it to lend WPPSS not money, but something just as valuable—its AAA credit rating. With this behind them, the utilities had little trouble finding underwriters for an initial bond issue or customers for the bonds themselves.[2]

But the project, which initially called for the construction of three reactors near the southeastern Washington town of Richland, quickly grew. Construction of the first reactor had barely begun before WPPSS decided to expand its nuclear program and add two more reactors, these to be built two hundred miles west of Richland at Satsop. With the expansion of WPPSS's plans came an expansion of the system itself, which quickly grew to include 115 utilities in eight western states.

The program, which would have provided power customers with a whopping 6,000 megawatts of electricity, proved too much for WPPSS and the small-town businessmen who sat on its board of directors. They simply could not handle the task of building five state-of-the-art plants simultaneously at a time when interest rates were rising and regulations on nuclear plant safety were growing stricter and stricter. Construction costs soared, throwing WPPSS's carefully calculated projections into a cocked hat. WPPSS responded to the rising costs by issuing new bonds.[3]

But the bond issues, while providing cash, did not solve the consortium's construction problems. Completion dates slipped, schedules and timetables had to be revised. Public opposition, mainly but not exclusively from people who wanted desperately to preserve the pristine character that makes the Northwest so attractive, developed and grew continually stronger. And, worst of all from the utilities' point of view, the whole reason for building the plants began to evaporate as demand for electricity in the Northwest fell far below the 7 percent a year increase upon which WPPSS had based its decision to build the plants. Instead, it grew at a mere 1 percent a year.

Everything that could go wrong with WPPSS seemed to go wrong. Union problems arose, stalling work on the plants. Bad weather slowed construction even more. Inept management, most of it by people with no experience of nuclear plant construction or management, slowed things even further. By the late seventies, the project was a full five years behind schedule. By 1980, when a new management team was brought in by a WPPSS board desperate to keep construction on some sort of schedule, the project was faltering even more. In March 1981, WPPSS offered what turned out to be the final sale of bonds to finance the construction of its Number 4 and Number 5 plants. The offering of $200 million was rated A-1 by Moody's Investors service, A+ by Standard and Poor's Corporation—the third-highest rating of each agency and a sign that WPPSS's desirability as an investment was falling. A few months later, WPPSS Managing Director Robert Ferguson announced that the consortium had recalculated the cost of the project, which had been placed at $6.67 billion when construction started in 1972, $15.9 billion when progress had been evaluated in 1978. The estimated cost of completion, Ferguson said, had gone up again. It now stood at $23.9 billion, or almost four times the original estimate. Ferguson called for a "moratorium" on the construction of Number 4 and Number 5. The board went along with his request. A short time later, work was stopped on the two plants. It did not resume.[4]

By 1983 it was obvious that WPPSS was in deep trouble. The consortium had been scrambling for almost two years to meet its obligations on its bonds. By April the word was out that WPPSS would be unable to make a $15.6 million debt service payment to New York's Chemical Bank on bonds worth $2.25 billion that had been issued to finance the two plants that had been scrapped. The word frightened people in the country's financial world, for it suggested that WPPSS might not be able to complete the three other plants, on which a total of $6.1 billion was owed. The word frightened them, too, because the uncertainty that a default would create would certainly shake the foundations of the entire municipal bond market and lead to huge losses for big and small investors alike. Wall Streeters compared the impending default to the near default by New York City, which in 1975 came close to failing to make its debt service payment. And they awaited the date upon which WPPSS would either pay or default with tangible trepidation. "This situation is another Mount St. Helens waiting to happen," said one brokerage firm economist.[5]

His analysis was accurate.

WPPSS was a financial house of cards. The utilities in the Pacific Northwest, which had agreed to use power from plants Number 4 and Number 5 and which were supposed to help finance the project, were the very companies pushing the consortium toward default. They had signed contracts, known as "take or pay" agreements, that obligated them to pay for the reactors whether they ever generated any electricity or not. By the spring of 1983, the utilities were claiming that the contracts were unenforceable and that they had been misled by official projections about future energy shortages. Most of the utilities had long since stopped making any payments to WPPSS. By the end of June, they owed the consortium a total of $62.4 million.[6]

The utilities were not the only ones pushing WPPSS toward default. WPPSS's woes had also made a great many enemies among Washington's electric consumers. Since bills for the nuclear plants had first started coming due, residential electric rates in Washington had gone up an average of 80 percent. Many irate ratepayers urged that WPPSS file for bankruptcy so that its debt payments could be eased and their monthly burdens lightened.[7]

In the end it seemed that even the courts were conspiring against WPPSS. In late spring, in a major and unexpected decision, the Washington State Supreme Court freed Washington utilities from their obligations to help pay the $2.25 billion bill for the canceled nuclear plants.

The court's decision sealed WPPSS's fate. "Default is now pretty much assured," said Senator Al Williams, chairman of the Washington State Energy Committee, "and bankruptcy is much more likely."[8]

Bankruptcy, as it turned out, was more than just likely; it was inevitable. At the time of the court decision, WPPSS had barely enough in its bank account to pay its upcoming interest charges of $93.7 million. But paying those charges would clean out its account. Only a federal bailout seemed likely to save WPPSS, and Washington showed no interest in repeating the Chrysler experience.

In July 1983, therefore, the inevitable happened. WPPSS defaulted. Its default threw the $400 billion municipal bond market into turmoil, driving down prices and raising borrowing costs for both state and local governments. It also raised serious questions about the ability of utilities to manage construction of nuclear power plants.

The industry might have weathered the WPPSS debacle had what happened in the state of Washington been an aberration, an ailment unique to one collection of companies in the Pacific Northwest. Unfortunately for the industry, it was not. WPPSS's problems were endemic to the whole industry, which was plagued by bad judgment, bad management, and bad luck. In the months following the WPPSS default, many U.S. utilities tried their best to dismiss the consortium's collapse as a freak, assuring the public—and particularly their investors—that "it can't happen to our company." Their assurances, however, were unconvincing, like the jaunty whistling of a pedestrian passing a graveyard on a moonless night. What happened to WPPSS could happen to other U.S. utilities, and it soon did, in what members of the industry themselves subsequently described as "the crash of '84."

The first sign of the impending crash came early in January. It came in Illinois, where Commonwealth Edison, the broad-shouldered giant that obtained 45 percent of its power from nuclear plants, had just completed work on its Byron 1 plant, half of a two-reactor complex. Com Ed had good reason to be pleased with Byron. The GE-designed boiling water reactor had been built in just ten years, a good two or three less than the national average. Its $3.7-billion price tag was also below the national average, making the company think that it had built itself a bargain.

The company also thought that it had built itself a rather good plant. So when it asked the NRC for permission to begin loading fuel so that it could put the reactor into operation, it expected approval to come automatically.

Its expectation proved unrealistic. Announcing that it had "no confidence" in the quality-control procedures used in overseeing some of the plant's construction, the NRC denied Com Ed's application. The NRC action, based in part on testimony from Illinois environmental and consumer groups, was unprecedented. No utility had ever before been denied a license to operate a nuclear plant it had completed, and the knowledge that one could be denied to operate a $3-billion plant shook the nuclear industry to its very foundations. Com Ed asked the Illinois Commerce Commission to approve a $502.1 million annual raise in rates to cover the start-up costs of Byron 1. The prospect of a delay forced the company to withdraw its request and to consider asking for an even bigger hike if the delay in obtaining a license persisted. That a rate hike would be needed to keep Com Ed solvent was obvious. The idle Byron plant was costing the company $30 million a month.[9]

Com Ed's problems were bad enough. But other problems were soon to follow. Only three days after the NRC's decision to deny Com Ed a license, the first of them did.

This time, the site of the problem was Indiana, where the Public Service Company had been building a nuclear plant on the banks of the Ohio River near Madison. The installation, known as the Marble Hill plant, was PSI's first nuclear plant. The company, which served

540,000 consumers, had obtained 97 percent of its power from coal. But back in 1973, with demand for electricity up, a coal strike just settled, and nuclear power looking like a bargain, PSI decided to go nuclear.

Its decision had not been warmly welcomed. Opposition from environmentalists and people worried about nuclear plant safety dragged the process of getting a construction permit out for five years. Construction had barely begun before quality control problems began to surface. Construction crews that were supposed to repair the air pockets that inevitably occur in concrete while it is being poured were lax in performing their jobs, so concrete structures cracked. In August 1979 construction on all safety-related parts of the plant were halted on order of the NRC. In December 1980, after the company had assembled an expanded staff of nuclear power plant experts, the NRC allowed safety-related work to continue. By April 1982 construction work was back in full swing.

But bigger trouble lay just ahead. Back in 1973 PSI had estimated the cost of building Marble Hill at around $1 billion and had figured on getting the twin units operational in 1982 and 1984. But as had happened with so many other nuclear projects, the dollar figures grew and the completion dates kept getting pushed back. Within a short time, the cost of the plant rose to $5.1 billion; the operating dates were moved back to 1986 and 1987. Then, in October 1983, PSI announced that due to the financial strain it was suffering, it would have to further slow its construction schedule; it changed the cost estimate for Marble Hill to $7 billion, the completion dates to 1988 and 1990. PSI laid off 4,500 workers, a move that devastated the economy of the area. It saw the ratings for its bonds drop to speculative status. It saw its debts piling up. In 1983, with income of $875 million against a debt load of $1.5 billion, PSI faced the unpleasant fact that it would be unable to borrow any more money to keep Marble Hill going. So it did what utilities usually do in such a situation. It sought rate relief.

PSI's first action was to try to persuade the Indiana legislature to change the law that prohibits utilities from asking for rate increases to cover CWIP, or construction work in progress. After the legislature overwhelmingly turned down its request, it asked the Indiana Public Service Commission to approve a "rate trending plan" that would have allowed the company to increase its rates 8 percent a year for five years. The proposal triggered such an outcry from consumers that Governor Robert Orr intervened. He ordered PSC hearings suspended and appointed a special blue-ribbon panel to study the matter.

It took the governor's task force, a panel of experts backed by advisers from the consulting firm of Arthur D. Little, Inc., and analysts from the Wall Street firm of Salomon Brothers, six months to complete its work. The results were not reassuring to PSI. Releasing the task force's summary report, Orr said that "rate payers should not be asked to share in the cost of Marble Hill unless it is in their long term benefit to do so." The task force report made it clear that it was not. It concluded that the Marble Hill plant would not be needed before 1993 at the earliest and said that it would cost more than $7.5 billion to complete. It recommended that the plant not be finished. Just as bad from PSI's point of view, it recommended that PSI and its shareholders absorb the major portion of the project's cost.

PSI was dismayed, to put it mildly. It felt that the task force was out to penalize the company and said that "penalizing Public Service . . . will actually hurt a lot more people, including customers, than it helps."

But, having registered its protest, PSI bowed to economic *force majeure*. Reluctantly, it announced that it was pulling out of the project, which had been half completed at a cost of $2.5 billion, slashing stockholder dividends 65 percent, from 72 cents a quarter to 25 cents. It also announced that it would file with the state's Public Service Commission for emergency rate relief, and ask for permission to raise its rates by 14 percent. "The board continues to believe that the Marble Hill station will be needed to meet future power requirements," said Hugh A. Barker, chairman of the utility. "But given the realities of today's political environment and financial markets, Public Service of Indiana clearly cannot continue to be a part of the project." [10]

PSI's decision to drop its Marble Hill project and take its losses generated page-one headlines in newspapers around the country and triggered a spate of stories suggesting that the nuclear power industry was on the ropes. Confirmation that the stories were on target came a few days later in the form of an announcement from Ohio.

Cincinnati Gas and Electric Company, which served the southern half of Ohio, was a big company and an ambitious one. So it had seemed only natural when, back in 1969, it announced that it would build a nuclear plant in Moscow, thirty miles southeast of Cincinnati on the Ohio River. The company hoped to have the plant, originally budgeted for $240 million, completed in 1975.

But construction of the William H. Zimmer plant had barely begun before troubles started. There were reports of construction workers drinking on the job. There were stories that the workers were using drugs, making belt buckles out of stainless-steel pipe on the company's time, stories that a prostitution ring was being run from the construction site. There were reports of shoddy workmanship, of concrete mix thinned to make it stretch farther, of sloppy welding on pipes designed to carry radioactive water. Construction of all safety-related components was halted in November 1982 by a three-to-two vote of the NRC, which said that the plant was of indeterminate quality.

The quality, though, was not all that was indeterminate. The completion date and the cost of the plant were just as difficult to pin down. As the years went by, Zimmer's completion date slipped to 1986. Its estimated completion cost climbed to $3.2 billion. As 1983 ended, CG&E found itself strapped. The rating on its bonds had dropped. Public opposition to completion of the Zimmer station had solidified. CG&E's two partners in the project, the Dayton Power and Light Company and the Columbus and Southern Ohio Electric Company, which together with Cincinnati had sunk $1.4 billion into the plant, wanted out. So did the two communities that the plant would be expected to serve. In mid-January 1984, the city councils of both Cincinnati and Covington, Kentucky, voted to recommend that the plant not be completed.

CG&E, its credit crumbling, scrambled around, trying to borrow money to finish the plant, which it said was 97 percent complete. But a few days after the two city council votes, it threw in the towel. The company announced that it would not attempt to complete Zimmer as a nuclear plant. Instead, it said, it would try to convert the installation to a coal-fired plant. It would, CG&E said, be cheaper to convert Zimmer to coal than it would be to spend the $1.8 billion necessary to complete it as a nuclear plant.[11]

The scrapping of the Zimmer plant was viewed by many as a fatal shot at the nuclear power industry. The cancellation of another plant a few days later was viewed as the coup de grace.

The Philadelphia Electric Company had been struggling to complete the second of its two Limerick reactors thirty miles west of its home city. But it had been getting deeper into debt as it did. In

1983 the Pennsylvania Public Service Commission told the company to cancel or suspend work on the project unless it could be financed internally. In January 1984, the company complied. Noting that the cost of the Limerick project had climbed from an original projection of $1.4 billion to more than $6 billion, Philadelphia Electric took the only way open to it and announced that it would suspend construction of Limerick 2 for eighteen months, laying off some 2,200 construction workers involved with the project. The company's statement did not say that Limerick 2 was dead. But no one familiar with Philadelphia Electric's situation thought otherwise.[12]

Plant cancellations, though, were not the only troubles facing the nuclear power industry as 1984 got under way. The companies that were forced to cancel plants were only the most serious cases in an industry plagued with an epidemic of insolvency. From New Hampshire to California, other companies were also in trouble. Among the most seriously ill were:

Public Service of New Hampshire. Eighty-eight percent complete at the beginning of 1984, Public Service's Seabrook Unit 1 was expected to be finished and ready to deliver power by July 1985. But no Granite Stater who valued the family farm seemed willing to bet it on such an event actually occurring. Seabrook's Unit 2, meanwhile, was only 28 percent complete and showing no signs of progressing a great deal farther. With no completion date set and with work proceeding at what the company called "minimum level," the project looked to outsiders as if it had ground to a halt. About the only thing still moving, in fact, was the line showing the increase in the Seabrook station's estimated cost. In January 1984, Public Service officials put the completion cost for Seabrook at $5.8 billion, or five times the plant's original cost.[13]

There seemed little likelihood that the company would recoup its investment. Company officials forecast that when Unit 1 went online it would be necessary to increase Public Service's rates from 40 to 50 percent just to cover start-up costs. Why? Because of a state law forbidding the utility from charging its ratepayers for the cost of constructing a plant until they were receiving its power. "It's unfortunate," said company spokesperson Myra Rivera. "We should be able to pass along some of the costs now. For every dollar the consumers didn't pay to cover CWIP [construction work in progress], it will eventually cost them eight dollars." That, she said, was the penalty for the delays and the consequent increased costs of borrowing money.[14]

But even then, company officials conceded, New Hampshire's consumers might not get all the power they were promised. For Public Service was considering canceling Seabrook Unit 2. At least a third of the sixteen utilities that had contributed to the construction of Seabrook, into which they had already poured $2.4 billion, voted in favor of forgetting about finishing the beleaguered—and unnecessary—addition. Indeed, Connecticut's Public Service Commission ordered the United Illuminating Company and Connecticut Light and Power to withdraw from their commitment to Unit 2.

Consumers Power Company of Michigan. Like other utilities, Consumers had grand ideas. When representatives of Consumers and Dow Chemical Company first began discussing plans for a nuclear plant in Midland, Michigan, they viewed it as one of the technological wonders of the world, a plant that would supply electric power for Consumers and steam for Dow's sprawling chemical works. The cost of the plant was originally estimated at $267 million, but as planning continued into 1968, the estimate was upped to $349 million. [15]

In 1969 Consumers began clearing the site for the massive plant along the banks of the Titabawassee River. But right from the start, construction problems, cost overruns, regulatory changes, and mismanagement threatened to doom the project. The construction problems started in 1970, even before Consumers had actually obtained an NRC license to build the plant, when the foundation for the reactor building was poured improperly. Construction was halted that same year after Congress approved the National Environmental Policy Act and the NRC forced Consumers to prepare an extensive environmental-impact statement. Other problems also developed. The soil of the flood plain on which the plant was being built proved too soft and porous. The generator building began to sink into the ground, forcing the utility to spend a fortune on drains and piers. Water seeped from a cooling pond into the construction site itself, further complicating construction. Defective welds had to be redone. "The quality of the problems here has been extraordinary," said Mary Sinclair, an outspoken opponent of nuclear power who had followed the Midland project from its inception. "Consumers has kept going in the face of all common sense. They can't admit they're wrong. I think their egos are involved."

As problems persisted, the cost of the Midland plant climbed. By the midseventies, the project's cost had crept up to $1.67 billion. By the summer of 1983, Dow Chemical decided that it had had enough.

Using an escape clause written into its contract for steam from the plant, the chemical company announced that it was pulling out of the project because it was clear that it was not going to be finished by the end of 1983. Dow asked Midland for more than $60 million in damages and accused Consumers of concealing the seriousness of the construction problems at the plant.

Consumers responded to Dow's charge with a demand of its own—that Dow pay between $340 and $470 million in penalties that were to be assessed in the event the chemical company canceled the thrice-negotiated contract for steam.[16]

Consumers did not cancel its Midland plant, which was 85 percent complete at the time of the "January massacre." But it did admit that it might be forced to scrub the plant, into which it had already sunk $3.4 billion, if it could not raise the $1 billion necessary to finish it. It also disclosed that the company's long-term debt exceeded the company's shareholders equity by more than $1 billion. Finally, it revealed that more than just Consumers could be in trouble if the company found that it could not finish the plant. Consumers Chairman John D. Selby warned that if the plant could not be finished and the company kept from getting back something on its investment, the utility, which served 1.2 million natural gas and 1.3 million electric customers, could be forced into bankruptcy.[17]

Long Island Lighting Company. Overlooking Long Island Sound on the North Shore of Long Island, the Shoreham plant was supposed to cost $241 million when LILCO first started it in 1968. But the beginning of 1984 found the plant, upon which the utility had already spent more than $3 billion, expected to cost well over $4 billion to finish. It also found the facility ten years behind schedule.[18]

Part of LILCO's problem, of course, could be attributed to opposition. Opponents of the plant, raising questions about safety, siting, and related matters, slowed the bureaucratic wheels and helped to stretch out the time required to complete Shoreham. The opponents got some help from Long Island politicians and administrators who moved with something less than dispatch when it came to helping the utility work out a plan for evacuating people in the area in the event of an accident. Suffolk County, in which the plant is located, moved in late 1983 to block its operation on the ground that it was not possible to work out an adequate emergency plan for the area.

But environmentalist opposition was hardly the only reason the plant took so long to complete. Regulatory changes, particularly those that resulted from the investigations of the accident at Three Mile Island, forced expensive additions and rescheduling of much of the work that had already been done at the plant. Shoddy workmanship forced NRC inspectors to require that certain parts of the plant be ripped out and redone.

Nor did LILCO's customers, who already paid one of the highest electricity rates in the U.S., welcome the idea of the company's putting the 800-megawatt plant on-line. LILCO admitted that it would have to raise its rates still further, maybe by as much as 50 percent, to help pay the costs of getting Shoreham into operation.

By midsummer, though, the debate had moved beyond the question of whether Shoreham should open. With bankruptcy stalking LILCO and political opponents snapping at the utility's heels, the major question became one of determining exactly who could be held responsible for turning a $4 billion investment into a monument to misjudgment. LILCO, paying $40 million a month in interest charges, insisted that the plant should be allowed to run. But its insistence, in the face of opposition by ratepayers, politicians, and environmentalists, seemed less a plea to get things going at the plant than an attempt to lay the groundwork for a lawsuit against the state, an action in which LILCO would seek some sort of financial relief.[19]

The company's desperation was understandable. LILCO had few alternatives to opening up the plant. Continuing the legal fight while the plant sat idle was expensive. But so was simply mothballing the plant and letting it sit in storage until such time as it was needed. Neither would exempt the company, which had already stopped making tax payments, from making interest and loan payments to the banks from which it had borrowed so heavily. Nor would anything help the company's stockholders, who had already seen their dividends disappear and the value of their holdings drop dramatically. "It's a no-win situation," said the utility's chairman, Dr. William Catacosinos, who was brought in to run the company following the February resignation of his predecessor. "About the only thing that won't cripple us economically is starting up the plant and using it to produce electricity, and that's the thing we are not being allowed to do."[20]

The impact of both the cancellations and the enormous cost overruns on those companies that had not canceled their plants was enormous. The ratings on utility company bonds had dropped dramatically, making them unattractive as investments and further hampering the beleaguered companies as they attempted to raise money to complete construction projects. Many investment analysts and brokers began warning their customers away from utility stocks and bonds, hoping to protect them from the effects of expected bankruptcies. Consumers also had cause to worry as faltering utilities sought to pass the costs of building their expensive and often unnecessary plants on to the very people they were expected to provide with inexpensive electricity.

What had gone wrong? Why was the industry in such parlous condition? William Dickhoner, president of Cincinnati Gas and Electric, saw the industry as a victim of outside forces. "It's not the president, it's not the contractor or anyone else," he told *Time* magazine. "The common denominator is the NRC. You can't build something when you have 285 regulatory changes while it's being built. Some components have been rebuilt three or four times out there. The NRC has got to change or nuclear is just plain dead. It's almost a punitive deal to open a nuclear plant anymore. I didn't want to leave my successors with the problems of operating a nuclear plant for 30 years."[21]

Others in the industry expressed similar sentiments, suggesting that, if only the NRC and the environmentalists would leave them alone, utilities could bring nuclear plants onto line for less money than it was costing them as the decade of the eighties approached its midpoint.

But others recognized that most of the blame lay with the industry itself. Douglas Cassel, an attorney for an Illinois citizens' group, noted that the industry rushed into a complex technology before it had fully mastered its arcana. He said: "The utilities failed to take into account the technological complexity and fragility of nuclear power and the unavoidable problem that humans have to build, operate, and inspect a nuclear plant. If we were all top engineers who never got sleepy, then maybe nuclear power would work the way it's supposed to in the physics books." Former NRC Commissioner Victor Gilinsky agreed. "It is clear that we got ahead of ourselves in expanding and scaling up the applications of nuclear power as fast as we did," he said. "These plants take a lot more care than anyone originally thought."[22]

Others agreed that changing regulations complicated construction, requiring the redrawing of plans and the refitting of installations already built. But most agreed that the changes were necessary and charged the companies themselves with both rigidity and bad management. Acting as general contractors, utility companies with little or no expertise in designing and building nuclear plants frequently got in over their heads, and once in, allowed pride and a feeling that they were best qualified to solve their own problems prevent them from seeking outside help. They also performed poorly when it came to supervising plant construction and allowed subcontractors to get away with substandard work in the hope that it would not be noticed, rather than correcting it on the spot.

Whatever its causes, though, the crash of '84 left the nuclear industry reeling. Some critics, in fact, believed that the industry had suffered a blow from which it would not, could not, recover. Were they right? Was nuclear power finished in the U.S.?

There was no question that the January massacre had left the U.S. nuclear industry in critical condition. But not even nuclear power's most ardent opponents would agree that the industry's condition was terminal. "I think it will come back," said then-Energy Secretary Donald Hodel. "I think eventually the U.S. will say that we need a nuclear component."[23]

What he did not say, though, was how—or when.

Ten

Energy for the Future

There is an old nautical axiom that warns would-be mariners never to throw away a piece of rope. "You may," cautions the old salt, "need it later."

The same warning could well be applied to nuclear power. It may not seem necessary, or even desirable, to people frightened by the accident at Three Mile Island, or to consumers burdened with rising bills as a result of nuclear plant projects that have cost many times the figures originally calculated for their construction. It may not seem necessary to those who can see that utilities already have more than enough capacity to meet American energy needs, not only for the present, but for the immediate future. It may not seem necessary to those who feel that there are cheaper, safer, less risky methods of generating electric power.

Nuclear power may not seem necessary right now because it is not. The U.S. does not need nuclear power, or at least more nuclear power than it presently possesses, now, in the middle of the eighties. It seems unlikely to need any more than it now has much before the end of the century.

But if population and economic growth continue even at their present slow rates, and if the demand for electric power continues to increase even at its present low rate of 2 or 3 percent a year, some growth in U.S. generating capacity is going to be necessary. The utilities' present reserve capacity of 25 percent can quickly disappear if the demand for electricity should for any one of a number of reasons suddenly increase sharply.

Where, though, will the U.S. obtain this energy? The country has exploited all available hydroelectric resources. Most rivers capable of providing large amounts of hydroelectric power have been dammed; the few large rivers left undammed can, for the most part, provide only limited quantities of energy. They may also be better used for other purposes, like recreation and development of other resources such as farms and forests. Proposals to dam Maine's scenic St. John River, for example, were abandoned after environmentalists acquainted the public with the fact that turning one of the country's most beautiful rivers into a muddy lake would still provide only a few peak hours of power a day. Residents of North Carolina successfully fought plans to dam the New River for the same reason. The demands on western rivers are already greater than most of them can handle. There is, as experts have emphasized, only a limited amount of water in the western U.S. The resources currently known can support population; they can support agriculture; they can support mining and oil refining; they can provide energy. But they cannot do all four simultaneously, which means that those who would use them must make choices and assign priorities, determining which uses of western water resources are the most important, and weighing the competing demands of those who want to use them for drinking, for irrigating fields, for supporting activities like mining or shale oil extraction, or for generating power.

Most energy experts, therefore, tend to rule out rivers when it comes to generating large amounts of electricity. But what, then, does this leave?

Several sources, say advocates of alternative energy sources. It leaves solar and wind power, tidal power, geothermal power, thermonuclear fusion, and coal.

Their point is well made. All of these sources hold out at least the promise of providing the U.S. with at least some of the energy it is going to need in the future. But are all of these alternative sources truly viable? A realist would have to answer, "Not really."

Take solar power, for example. There is no question that the heat of the sun can be captured and used to heat and cool homes, to boil water, and to run machinery. Thousands of Americans have installed solar panels on their rooftops and use the energy they collect to heat water and to warm their homes. Energy experts agree, in fact, that anyone who builds a new home without at least attempting to employ some sort of solar technology is wasting much of his money.

Solar energy is definitely efficacious on a small scale and has proved its practicality in private homes, office buildings, and other individual installations. But can solar provide the large amounts of electricity that Americans need and want? It certainly cannot do so at the present time. Experimental solar power stations thus far constructed by the U.S. Energy Department and its research contractors have been too small to be considered replacements for the 1,000-megawatt plants that utilities find practical for providing power. And, say researchers, they are not likely to get bigger for quite a while. But they will have to if they are going to compete with other sources of electricity. Given the current state of solar technology, say energy experts, it would take an array of mirrors and collectors covering several hundred acres to produce the amount of electricity now produced by even the smallest of existing nuclear or coal-fired plants. Meeting the energy needs of a substantial segment of the U.S. population might require a "solar farm" nearly the size of the state of Arizona.

There is no question that a solar power plant, even one of such monumental size, would be clean. But it is naive to assume that using solar on a large scale would be entirely without effect on the environment. The earth's "weather machine" is, after all, driven largely by the sun, which heats some parts of the earth more than others, producing the temperature and pressure differentials that in turn generate the planet's winds, storm systems, and cloud cover. There is no reason to assume that preventing sunlight from striking a significant section of the earth's surface would not have at least some impact on the environment.

Wind power also offers some alternatives to more conventional sources of energy. The Dutch have traditionally used windmills to run the pumps that help them stay ahead in their constant battle against the sea. Farmers across the U.S. have long used small windmills to catch the breezes and take on the task of pumping water up from wells or aquifers. Some experiments undertaken in the U.S. under the auspices of the Energy Research and Development Administration have suggested that large windmills, some of them equipped with rotors more than one hundred feet long, can harness the wind effectively and generate electricity. But these huge windmills have proved themselves to be prone to mechanical problems (one wind turbine at Rocky Flats, Colorado, had an embarrassing tendency to be blown down whenever the wind blew strongly enough to really spin its rotors), and even when they function properly, they work, of course, only when the wind happens to be blowing.

Tapping the natural heat of the earth could also provide another source of energy. Iceland, which happens to sit atop one of the most active volcanic areas in the world, has long used its underground hot springs to heat its buildings, which is why no pall of smoke ever hangs over the country's capital of Reykjavik. A California utility has tapped hot springs at an area outside San Francisco known as The Geysers. Geothermal formations exist in other states as well, such as Montana and some parts of the Southwest, and there is no reason why utilities should not attempt to exploit these clean, pollution-free energy sources. But there is no reason, either, why anyone should expect geothermal sources to provide more than a minuscule amount of the energy that the U.S. needs now or will need in the future. There simply are not enough such sources sufficiently close to the earth's surface to be exploited economically.

Tidal power also seems attractive to those eager to see the U.S. avoid relying upon nuclear power for its energy. Advocates of this form of energy have long urged the creation of a tidal dam in the Bay of Fundy, between Maine and Nova Scotia, where some of the highest tides in the world occur twice daily. They propose construction of a sort of "floating dam," whose turbines would be spun by these tremendous tides, generating power that could then be fed into the national power system. The idea of harnessing the tides is certainly appealing, though it may also be extremely expensive. But doing so would not be without its environmental effects, either. Fishermen in both Maine and Nova Scotia have already raised questions about how the existence of a tidal dam might affect ocean currents or patterns of fish migration. Advocates of a tidal dam have not yet been able to answer them.

Many opponents of nuclear fission believe that the answer to America's energy problems might be found in fusion. This is essentially the opposite of nuclear fission, in which the nuclei of heavy atoms of uranium are split to release a neutron and generate energy. In fusion, atoms of light elements like hydrogen are fused or forced together to release an energy-producing neutron and, in the process, produce helium. The appeal of fusion is enormous. The hydrogen extractable from ordinary seawater could theoretically provide all the power the world would ever need indefinitely. The by-product of the fusion reaction could be used, as Princeton University Physicist Melvin Gottlieb has said, "to fill children's balloons."

But the problems that have thus far made fusion seem like little more than a physicist's pipe dream are formidable. Achieving a fusion reaction is a complicated process. The hydrogen or deuterium, a slightly heavier form of the element, must first be converted into a plasma, a sort of gas composed of stripped, or ionized, atoms. This plasma must then be confined at a certain density and for a certain amount of time. It must also be heated to a certain temperature before the atoms can begin colliding with each other and fusing. Confining the plasma, which is done in a sort of magnetic bottle called a torus, has proved difficult ("We've learned a lot of things about plasmas, most of them unpleasant," says Gottlieb). Getting the right combination of density, time, and temperature has proved next to impossible. Neither researchers at Princeton, where a large experimental torus has been constructed, nor at the Soviet Union's scientific institutes, which have been cooperating with their U.S. counterparts in fusion studies, have been able to achieve a "break-even" reaction—one that produces as much power as is required to start it, in the laboratory. Until they do, there is no point in their even thinking about designing or building commercial fusion reactors.

When might they begin such a task? Fusion researchers asked this question generally reply by answering, "Fifteen years." But they also smile when they offer this answer. For fusion researchers have been giving this answer for at least fifteen years, leading their colleagues to suggest that they have come up with a new physical constant, the "fifteen-year constant."

This means that, at least for the foreseeable future, Americans who want abundant electrical energy are going to have to depend upon two sources—fossil fuels and nuclear power. And the choice among fossil fuels is limited. Oil and natural gas are too expensive to be burned to generate electric power. Natural gas is too valuable as a home heating fuel; oil is too valuable as a fuel for automobiles and aircraft and as a feedstock for the chemical industry. Utilities that own oil- or gas-fired plants are trying hard to phase them out and replace them with other types of installations. No utility has any plans to build new oil or gas plants.

So this means that the choice, at least for the short term, comes down to coal. There is no question that coal can be attractive. For one thing, it is abundant. The U.S.'s known coal reserves are among the world's largest; they will, at least at current rates of consumption, last more than two hundred years. Coal plants are certainly safer in several important ways than nuclear plants. Even after the control rods have been reinserted into the core, a nuclear plant continues to produce heat. Hours after a reactor has been shut down, decay still produces several kilowatts of heat. But shutting down a coal plant is simple. All an operator has to do is stop shoveling coal into the boiler.

Cheaper and faster to build, and able, under current conditions, to produce electricity more economically than nuclear plants, coal-fired plants will unquestionably provide an increasing amount of the energy Americans use during the remainder of the century. But they will also be responsible for some of the problems that Americans experience as well. For coal is not clean. Coal-burning plants pump thousands of tons of sulfur dioxides and other pollutants into the atmosphere each day. These sulfur dioxides combine with moisture in the atmosphere and eventually precipitate out as sulfuric acid, the primary ingredient of the so-called "acid rain" that is slowly destroying many U.S. and Canadian lakes and that may also be damaging forest areas in both countries.

Coal-burning plants, in fact, are currently discharging a ton of sulfur dioxides into the atmosphere every five minutes, and these pollutants already are having an enormous effect upon human health and the environment. According to a study conducted by the National Academy of Sciences, the annual releases from a single large coal plant may be responsible for as many as 25 deaths, 60,000 cases of respiratory disease, and $25 million in property damage.[1]

The overall toll from coal burning is even higher. U.S. health officials attribute 50,000 deaths a year to air pollution, and say that as many as 20,000 of these fatalities are the result of coal burning. Bernard Cohen, a physicist who happens to be a strong advocate of nuclear power, feels that this last figure is too high, and believes that it should be halved to 10,000. But even if Cohen is correct, the indictment of coal is impressive. The scientists who researched the Rasmussen Report figured that only one out of five meltdowns would result in as many as 1,000 deaths, and that only one out of one hundred would cause as many as 10,000 fatalities. If the Rasmussen Report is right, it means that American nuclear plants would have to undergo twenty-five meltdowns a year to be as dangerous to human health as coal plants.[2]

Cohen's calculations are chilling. But even they are incomplete, for they fail to take into account the terrible tolls taken by coal mining. Deep mining, in which coal is extracted from underground seams, is dirty and dangerous. Hundreds of miners die each year, some as a result of mine accidents, more as a result of "black lung," a generally fatal ailment caused by the occupational hazard of inhaling coal dust. Surface, or strip, mining scars the face of the earth, turning fields and forests into barren moonscapes. Both forms of mining produce sulfur-laden tailings that leach into and destroy streams.

Nor does coal burning do away with the thing most people fear about nuclear power. The combustion of coal also releases radioactivity into the environment. Indeed, as few procoal antinuclear activists seem to acknowledge, it releases a great deal of radioactivity. By law, a coal plant is allowed to release more radionuclides per hour of operation than a properly run nuclear plant. In fact, a coal plant does.

Coal may seem like a panacea to those Americans who fear and oppose nuclear power. But its appeal could fade quickly if the U.S. begins mining, transporting, and burning greatly increased amounts of it to generate electricity. For even with modern antipollution equipment, coal plants are dirtier than nuclear plants.

Which means that nuclear power still has a future, or rather, that it can still have a future. For, compared with coal, nuclear power has much to offer. Properly managed, nuclear power is clean and far less likely to cause health problems than coal. Properly managed, nuclear power can provide energy economically. Properly managed, nuclear power can meet many of America's energy needs.

But how can it do this? How can the industry assure not only its survival but its revival? How can it regain its lost credibility, its vanishing viability? How can it heal its self-inflicted wounds and transform itself from an economic terminal case to an important ingredient of the U.S. energy mix?

Even the most ardent nuclear advocates admit that the industry must have some outside help if it is to survive. It must get that help from the federal government. But what must the government do— and more important, what should it do—to help the nuclear industry to help itself?

The most important thing the government can do is be honest— both with itself and the American public. It can begin this task by recognizing that it can no longer play a dual role with regard to nuclear power. It cannot function as a booster, or act as a sort of nuclear chamber of commerce, if it is also going to function as a regulator and guarantor of public safety. One role conflicts with the other.

There is only one way in which the government can resolve this conflict. It must make a choice, and there is no question as to what that choice must be. The government must abandon the role of cheerleader and leave the task of selling nuclear power to the industry itself. It must choose to regulate. More important, it must regulate well, placing the safety of the public before the economic health and welfare of the industry. It must show the public that it is concerned about safety, and it must do so by its actions, not its words.

The government can begin the second part of this task by dealing straightforwardly with the public. It must be frank about the dangers and risks posed by nuclear power, recognize and respond quickly to public concerns about radiation. The government must end the secrecy in which too many meetings of the Nuclear Regulatory Commission are still conducted. It must be honest and admit when it does not know the answers to the public's questions. Most important, the government must recognize that the decision as to whether the risks associated with nuclear power are worth accepting is one that the public alone can make. It is not a decision that can be imposed upon the public by scientists or government officials, no matter how good their intentions may be.

There are other steps the government can take to improve the U.S. energy situation. The government should not subsidize the nuclear power industry. It should not attempt to bail it out as it did the faltering Chrysler Corporation. If the industry cannot compete on its own, there is no reason why the U.S. taxpayer should be forced to pay to help keep it alive. But there are some steps the government can take to help the nuclear industry.

One way in which the government can help is by reforming the regulatory process. The current procedures for licensing nuclear power plants are both inefficient and unwieldy. They encourage interference, both serious and capricious, and they allow for endless delays, not all of which are necessary. The government should not relieve those who wish to build and operate nuclear power plants from the burden of demonstrating that their plants are necessary, well-built, and well managed. It should not relieve them of the obligation of placing public safety before corporate profits and recognizing that they are dealing with a complex technology that exacts a high price for carelessness. The government should not, on the other hand, deny those who object to nuclear plant construction—for whatever reason—an opportunity to voice their opinions and to express their opposition.

But the government should take some steps to streamline the regulatory process. There is no reason why the licensing process must drag on as long as it does, no reason why it should take twelve or more years to bring a nuclear power plant from the planning stage to the point where it can begin to produce power. There is no reason why the government should not be able to cut through the jungle of paperwork that can delay the construction of nuclear power plants and add so much to their costs. The government can help do something about this problem and it should.

If the government wants to make nuclear power acceptable, it must also do something about the problem of disposing of nuclear wastes.

The problem is a pressing one. Compared to coal plants, nuclear plants generate little in the way of waste. A 1,000-megawatt coal-fired facility produces thirty pounds of ash a second, which translates to a staggering 473,040 tons a year. The volume of high-level waste produced by the average nuclear plant would fit into the packing case for a large television set.

However, while coal ash is essentially inert and harmless, nuclear fuel rods are not. Contaminated by such fission products as strontium 90, cesium 137, and plutonium 239, these spent fuel rods are not only physically hot, but radioactively hot as well, and likely to remain that way for hundreds, maybe even thousands of years.

Disposing of these fuel rods has proved difficult. American nuclear plants have been storing their spent fuel rods temporarily in on-site "swimming pools." But a number of older plants are filling up their pools and running out of storage space. There is now more than 155,000 cubic feet of high-level waste cooling off at nuclear plants around the U.S. But twenty-seven years after the first commercial nuclear reactor went on-line at Shippingport, Pennsylvania, there is still no permanent disposal system in effect, and the public is becoming concerned. Concedes AIF President Carl Walske: "The public's chief concern about nuclear energy revolves around the storage problem."[3]

The problem is not insoluble, at least in theory. Scientists agree that the nuclear wastes currently sitting in pools at U.S. reactors could be vitrified, or sealed in glass, and permanently buried in underground caverns or salt formations. The volume of such wastes is not large, they note, and it could be further reduced if the U.S. began recycling the fuel rods, a process that would reclaim 97 percent of their fissile materials.[4]

But the theory has yet to be put into practice. Although the U.S.

currently has two sites for the disposal of such low-level wastes as contaminated tools and the radioactive materials used by hospitals, the country does not have a repository capable of handling spent fuel rods. Attempts to create such a facility as the low-level repository at Hanford, Washington, were halted when the Nuclear Regulatory Commission, the U.S. Geological Survey, the state of Washington, and the Yakima Indians all joined together to object because there were indications that the wastes were contaminating local rivers and streams. The site in North Carolina has been ruled out for high-level wastes.

The search for another site or sites has not yet produced results. In 1982 Congress passed the Nuclear Waste Policy Act, which charged the Department of Energy with setting up not one, but two nuclear waste dumps. Under the terms of the NWPA, the DOE must recommend three sites to the President before the end of 1985, and he must select one of them by early 1987. Government geologists have identified several potential sites, including formations in Arizona, New Mexico, Utah, Texas, Mississippi, and Louisiana. Nuclear plant owners, who pay a levy of one mill per kilowatt, have been contributing some $40 million a month to support the program.

But like just about everything else in the nuclear power industry, the program is behind schedule. The DOE said in 1983 that it would be at least three years late meeting the congressional deadline for making its recommendations to the President, which means that it will probably be 1990 before the President can make his decision. But not even Presidential action is likely to end America's search for a place to put its nuclear waste. The NWPA gives states the right to veto any federal site selections, and some states will probably exercise that option, for while everyone believes that the U.S. must have a nuclear waste repository, no one wants it in his backyard.

Still, the government is going to have to find someone willing to accept it. Until it does, a large number of Americans will remain unwilling to accept nuclear power.

Regulatory reform and a solution to the problem of nuclear waste disposal will go a long way toward helping the U.S. nuclear power industry to survive. But the most important steps must be taken not by the government, but by the industry itself.

One of the steps the industry can take is to adopt a standardized reactor design. At the present time, says Walske, "there are too many utilities and too many designs." His point is well made. Although not many members of the public realize it, each nuclear plant is different, custom-made for each utility in much the same way that a custom-made suit is made to order for each customer. This plethora of designs inevitably slows the licensing process because each new design has to be checked out individually. It also makes it inherently more difficult to improve the safety features of plants, because the experience gained on one reactor cannot readily be applied to another. In addition, it makes it harder to improve operating procedures, since the lessons learned by operating one plant cannot always be put into practice on other plants.

Adopting standardized reactor designs would eliminate these problems, as the experience of the French shows. The French build only two basic nuclear plants, a big one and a bigger one, and they bring their plants on-line far more quickly than do utilities in the U.S. "The French standardized," says Walske, "and through the process of repetition, they've greatly simplified the whole process. We in the U.S. indulged in the luxury of custom-made nuclear reactors. But we can't afford that luxury in the future."

Standardizing reactor design is not all that the nuclear countries of Europe and the Far East have done to make atomic energy acceptable. In addition to building and running their plants well, they have also shown that they are necessary. The Japanese, who have no native energy sources, for example, accept nuclear power because they know that there are no practical alternatives. The French and Germans accept it because their utilities have made nuclear power competitive with coal.

Those countries that have accepted the atom have also taken another important step: they have recognized that there is a difference between nuclear power and nuclear weapons. A significant portion of the young people who have taken to the streets to demonstrate against nuclear weaponry in Great Britain, France, and Germany have raised no objections to the construction of nuclear plants designed to use the atom peacefully. Nor have the Japanese, the only people ever actually subjected to a nuclear attack, failed to understand that the atom is not necessarily evil. Though the Japanese have protested vigorously against the presence in their harbors of U.S. ships carrying nuclear warheads, they continue to build nuclear plants to generate electricity.

Their understanding is important. There is a great difference between a nuclear power plant and a nuclear weapon. Europeans and Japanese understand this. Many Americans apparently do not, and insist upon linking nuclear power reactors with nuclear devices intended for less peaceful purposes. Their attitude is unfortunate, for it confuses the issue of nuclear disarmament, while denying Americans the energy that they may soon need.

The nuclear power industry can help correct this misconception by concentrating on using the atom to generate energy and by leaving questions about weapons to the government. The industry can help make nuclear power economically acceptable by abjuring the bad management of which many companies have been guilty. Bad planning was responsible for the decision to build many of the nuclear plants that have either been canceled or that have cost companies up to fifteen times as much as they were originally supposed to. Bad management also contributed to the huge cost overruns that have plagued the U.S. utility industry. The industry could help itself enormously by revamping its management procedures so that nuclear plant construction could be handled by a single experienced company rather than a loose and, all too often, loosely supervised coalition of subcontractors.

The industry could also help itself by studying the experience of its more successful operators, for their records prove that building and operating nuclear plants is not beyond the capacity of *all* U.S. utilities. The 830-megawatt Maine Yankee Atomic Power Plant in Wiscasset, for example, has operated reliably since it first went on-line in 1972. The plant established a world record for performance by working 392 consecutive days without a shutdown during 1977 and 1978, and was in service 79.3 percent of the time during 1983. The Yankee Atomic Electric plant in Rowe, Massachusetts has been producing 185 megawatts of electricity without incident since it first went on-line in 1961.[5]

Nor need nuclear plants be all that difficult to build. Florida Power and Light managed to bring its two St. Lucie plants onto line in seven and six years respectively. The Trojan plant, located on the Columbia River in Oregon, was completed in 1975, seven years after construction began, at a cost of just $460 million. It is currently providing some of the cheapest electricity in the U.S. and doing so while maintaining a good safety record.

Duke Power Company of North Carolina has done even better. Using a highly trained team of its own engineers to manage its projects, and eschewing the industry practice of relying on a congeries of outside contractors, it has managed to bring its nuclear plants to completion at prices well below the industry average. Duke brought its three Oconee plants onto line in 1973 and 1974 at an average cost of $194 per kilowatt, well below the prevailing industry average of $316. It has managed to stay under the average since then. In 1984, when the rest of the industry was finishing plants for a cost of $1,959 per kilowatt, Duke completed its McGuire 2 plant for $918 a kilowatt, an accomplishment that board chairman William States Lee attributes to careful supervision. "The art of managing a large project is to be self-critical, to find your mistakes early and do something about them," he said.[6]

Insisting on efficiency will help the nuclear industry to keep itself going. But if the industry is to survive, it must also become more sensitive to public concerns about safety. Bernard Cohen may be right when he writes that "the public has been driven insane over fear of radiation," or when he claims that "the public's understanding of radiation dangers has virtually lost all contact with the actual dangers as understood by scientists."[7] But the fact that he may be right does not change the fact that a large segment of the public and a significant number of scientists as well believe that radiation, even at low levels, is risky or that knowledge about its effects is incomplete. Most Americans know that nuclear plants cannot explode like atomic bombs; a study conducted in 1980 by the University of Michigan's Survey Research Center found that 8 percent of Americans knew that this was impossible, while 44 percent understood that it was unlikely.[8] But many Americans do feel that the radiation released by even well-run nuclear plants is a subtle hazard, and scientists have been unable to disabuse them of this belief. The public simply does not have enough information about low-level radiation.

Not having this information is bad enough. But the nuclear industry and pronuclear scientists have tended to make matters worse by attempting to downplay those risks that are known. Describing a risk as insignificant cannot help but make someone ask the question: Insignificant to whom? The probability that a nuclear accident will cause one or two additional cases of cancer in a population may seem insignificant to someone who deals in statistics. But it is anything but insignificant to those who may develop these cancers or die from them. "I resent it when someone in a corporate boardroom decides what risks I should accept," says a Pennsylvania woman who cannot look out her kitchen window without seeing the cooling towers of Three Mile Island. "I think that's pretty high-handed."

Others agree. They feel that both the industry and its scientific supporters have a cavalier attitude toward the public and its fears, and find, especially since Three Mile Island, that they do not trust either.

Their attitudes are understandable; no one likes it when others make their decisions for them, especially when those decisions may involve their health and safety. More particularly, no one likes it when others make their decisions about nuclear power, which has long been and is likely to remain a highly emotional issue. The decision as to which risks are acceptable is not one that the industry or the scientific community can make. The former can try to reduce those risks through careful construction and sound management. The latter can acquaint the public with the nature and extent of these risks. But the decision as to whether these risks are worth accepting is not a scientific question. It is a question of public policy and one that only the public can answer.

The distinction is one that Donald Hodel well understands. "We are applying a different safety test to nuclear power than we are to other activities," Hodel told *Time* early in 1984. But, he acknowledges, this is something the public has a right to do. "These are societal decisions," he says. "It's the right of a society to make those decisions. For better or worse, right now, we've decided that we want greater protection against radiation than against other comparable threats."

If this is what the public wants, then this is what it should get, and the nuclear industry should provide it. It should do so by recognizing the public's concerns about safety and by taking concrete, rather than cosmetic, steps to meet them.

For it is wrong, as some industry spokesmen have stated, to claim that the public simply will not accept risks. The public accepts risks all the time. It does so, however, only when it is convinced that these risks are offset by certain benefits. Americans all know, for example, that driving is dangerous, yet millions drive great distances each day either because they have no alternative or because they are convinced that the convenience of personal transportation offsets any risks. Americans know, too, that planes can and do crash. But this does not prevent a tremendous number of them from opting for the speed of air travel over the inconvenience of traveling by bus or train.

Americans will make a similar judgment with regard to nuclear power. The U.S. public is unlikely to consider the risks associated with nuclear power acceptable as long as nuclear plant construction means rising utility rates and expensive electricity. Nor is the public likely to consider nuclear power's risks reasonable while there are other alternatives and no compelling evidence that more nuclear plants are necessary. The public will, however, find nuclear's risks reasonable when it can see some proof that nuclear power is both essential and economical, when it is convinced that the advantages of having a nuclear plant for a neighbor outweigh the disadvantages of not having one.

It is up to the industry to provide this evidence. The best way it can provide it is through performance, not public relations. The industry does not now enjoy a good press. It will not be able to do so until it decides to be honest with both the press and the public, to admit its failings and to deal straightforwardly with its problems. Reams of releases will not convince the press or the public that nuclear power is safe, necessary, or desirable. Attacks on environmentalists and other antinuclear elements will not make Americans stop worrying and learn to love nuclear power. Performance and proof that nuclear plants can provide power safely and economically just might.

Battered, bloody, the U.S. nuclear power industry is definitely down. But it is not yet out. With no new plants on order, nuclear construction will come to a standstill once those plants presently in the pipeline are completed. The industry will go into a sort of holding pattern and remain in it for some years; neither General Electric nor Westinghouse, which are continuing to sell their reactors abroad, expects an order from a U.S. utility before the end of the decade at the earliest. No one associated with the industry expects that nuclear power will, as President Nixon once predicted, provide half of America's electricity by the year 2000. No one, in fact, expects the industry to expand much, if at all, for the remainder of the century.

But this does not mean that the industry must die. The slowdown gives it a chance to sink into the industrial equivalent of a coma. But it also gives it the chance to rebuild. U.S. reactor manufacturers can use the coming quiet period as a time to review their plant designs and to work on developing safer, more efficient plants, something Westinghouse is already doing. Utilities can use the interval to reexamine their organization and procedures, to reassess how nuclear plants fit into their overall plans for power generation and to figure out how to build and run them more efficiently. The government can use the time to review its regulations and to determine how they can be streamlined without sacrificing safety.

And the American public can use the interval, too, to determine what it wants in the way of energy and whether it wants the convenience of having it in abundant supply. If it considers its needs carefully, it is likely to conclude that nuclear power is necessary. The U.S. will probably never have to rely upon nuclear power to provide most of its energy. It will probably not need any more nuclear plants than it now has until after the turn of the century. But after that, the U.S. is likely to find that it does need nuclear power to provide a large portion of its electricity. For the simple fact is that Americans are addicted to energy. American consumers want to continue flicking on light switches and turning on appliances without worrying about where the power will come from. Americans want electricity to power their television sets and the video games that modern technology makes it possible to play on them. Americans need energy, and the American economy must have abundant energy if it is to continue growing. A strong U.S. cannot rely upon energy imported from abroad or depend upon energy supplies that can be cut off by either wars or the whims of foreign governments.

Not even the most optimistic advocates of the atom see a day when nuclear power will replace other energy sources, either now or in the future. But realists recognize that the U.S. will need a mixture of energy sources to meet the needs of its consumers and to drive its economy. Nuclear power must be part of that mixture. Without it, the U.S. will simply run out of energy.

Source Notes

One The Critical Mass

1. "Pulling the Nuclear Plug," *Time*, February 13, 1984.
2. "The Nuclear Industry in 1983: Buoyed by the Rising Tide," Atomic Industrial Forum, January 16, 1984.
3. "Pulling the Plug," *Time*.
4. Personal communication, January 18, 1984.
5. "Pulling the Plug," *Time*.
6. "Nuclear Industry," Atomic Industrial Forum.
7. Personal communication, January 22, 1984.
8. "Pulling the Plug," *Time*.
9. Ibid.
10. "List of Troubled Reactors Grows," *The New York Times*, January 17, 1984, p. D5.
11. "Pulling the Plug," *Time*.
12. Ibid.
13. Ibid.
14. "Deepening Nuclear Woes," *The New York Times*, January 17, 1984, p. D1.
15. Personal communication, January 18, 1984.
16. Personal communication, January 20, 1984.
17. "Pulling the Plug," *Time*.
18. Personal communication, January 1984.
19. Personal communication, January 1984.
20. Communication to *Time*, January 1984.

Two   In the Beginning . . .

1. Daniel Ford, *The Cult of the Atom: The Secret Papers of the Atomic Energy Commission* (New York: Touchstone/Simon and Schuster, 1982, 1984), p. 48.
2. Isaac Asimov, *Isaac Asimov's Biographical Encyclopedia of Science and Technology* (New York: Equinox, 1972), p. 19.
3. Ibid., p. 201.
4. Atomic Industrial Forum, background paper.
5. *The Nuclear Almanac: Confronting the Atom in War and Peace* (Reading, Mass.: Addison-Wesley Publishing Co., 1984), p. 21.
6. Ibid., p. 23.
7. Ibid., pp. 22–23.
8. Ibid., p. 23.
9. Atomic Industrial Forum, background paper.
10. *The Nuclear Almanac*, p. 24.
11. Ford, *Cult of the Atom*, pp. 19–26.
12. Ibid., p. 28.
13. *The Nuclear Almanac*, p. 26.
14. Ibid., p. 30.
15. Ibid., pp. 29–51.
16. Ford, *Cult of the Atom*, p. 24.
17. Ibid., p. 29.
18. Ibid., p. 30.
19. Ibid., p. 31.
20. Ibid., p. 20.
21. Ibid., p. 33.
22. Ibid.
23. Ibid., p. 35.
24. *The Nuclear Almanac*, pp. 53–65.
25. Ford, *Cult of the Atom*, pp. 40–41.
26. Ibid.
27. *The Nuclear Almanac*, p. 71.
28. Atomic Industrial Forum, background paper.
29. Ford, *Cult of the Atom*, p. 37.
30. Ibid., p. 36.
31. Ibid., p. 39.
32. Atomic Industrial Forum, background paper.
33. Ibid.
34. Ibid.
35. *The Nuclear Almanac*, p. 71.
36. Ibid., p. 70.

Three   The Troubled Childhood

1. Peter Pringle and James Spigelman, *The Nuclear Barons* (New York: Holt, Rinehart & Winston, 1981), p. 263.
2. Ibid., p. 264.

3. Ibid., pp. 264–65.
4. Ibid., pp. 266–67.
5. Ibid., pp. 268–70.
6. Ibid., p. 271.
7. Ibid., p. 272.
8. Ford, *Cult of the Atom*, pp. 65–66.
9. Ibid., p. 74.
10. *The Nuclear Almanac*, p. 72.
11. Ibid., p. 73.
12. Ford, *Cult of the Atom*, pp. 59–60.
13. Ibid., pp. 87–89.
14. Ibid., p. 44.
15. Ibid., p. 45.
16. Ibid., pp. 66–67.
17. Ibid., p. 69.
18. Ibid., pp. 74–80.
19. Ibid., pp. 80–82.

Four A Difficult Adolescence

1. Ford, *Cult of the Atom*, pp. 87–89.
2. Ibid., pp. 92–93.
3. Ibid., p. 93.
4. Ibid., pp. 93–95.
5. Ibid., p. 94.
6. Ibid., p. 101.
7. Ibid., pp. 114–15.
8. Ibid., p. 116.
9. Ibid., p. 119.
10. Ibid., pp. 124–26.
11. Ibid., pp. 133–35.
12. Ibid., pp. 135–40.
13. Ibid., pp. 140–43.
14. Ibid., pp. 145–54.
15. Ibid., p. 154.
16. *The Nuclear Almanac*, pp. 290–91.
17. Ford, *Cult of the Atom*, p. 160.
18. *The Nuclear Almanac*, pp. 73–75.
19. Ibid., p. 75.
20. Ford, *Cult of the Atom*, p. 42.

Five No Business Like Nuke Business

1. Pringle and Spigelman, *Nuclear Barons*, p. 322.
2. "Pulling the Plug," *Time*.
3. Ibid.
4. Pringle and Spigelman, *Nuclear Barons*, p. 322.

5. Ibid.
6. Ibid., pp. 323–24.
7. Ibid., pp. 324–27.
8. Ibid., p. 325.
9. Ibid., p. 326.
10. Ibid., pp. 327–28.
11. Ibid., pp. 329–31.
12. Ibid., p. 339.
13. Ibid., pp. 337–45.
14. Ibid., pp. 346–56.
15. Personal communications during visit to U.S.S.R., September 1978.
16. Anthony J. Parisi, "Hard Times for Nuclear Power," *The New York Times Magazine*, December 15, 1983, pp. 36–38.
17. "Pulling the Plug," *Time*.
18. Parisi, "Hard Times," *The New York Times Magazine*.
19. Pringle and Spigelman, *Nuclear Barons*, pp. 357–58.
20. "The San Jose Three," *Time*, February 16, 1976.
21. Pringle and Spigelman, *Nuclear Barons*, p. 358.
22. Ibid., pp. 358–59.
23. Ibid., pp. 371–72.
24. "The Siege of Seabrook," *Time*, May 16, 1977.
25. Pringle and Spigelman, *Nuclear Barons*, p. 359.

Six A Rude Awakening

1. R. L. Weber, *A Random Walk in Science* (London: The Institute of Physics, 1973), p. 118.
2. "A Nuclear Nightmare," *Time*, April 9, 1979.
3. *The Nuclear Almanac*, p. 293.
4. Corrine Browne and Robert Munroe, *Time Bomb: Understanding the Threat of Nuclear Power* (New York: William Morrow and Co., 1981), pp. 155–56.
5. *The Nuclear Almanac*, p. 292.
6. Ibid., pp. 292–93.
7. Ibid., p. 294.
8. Personal communication during visit to U.S.S.R., September 1978.
9. *The Nuclear Almanac*, p. 292.
10. Ford, *Cult of the Atom*, pp. 217–20.
11. "The Irrational Fight Against Nuclear Power," *Time*, September 25, 1978.
12. "Life: An Atom-Powered Shutdown," *Time*, March 26, 1979.
13. Mike Gray and Ira Rosen, *The Warning* (New York: W. W. Norton, 1982), pp. 19–21.
14. Ibid., pp. 83–85.
15. Ibid., pp. 85–92.
16. "A Nuclear Nightmare," *Time*.
17. Gray and Rosen, pp. 100–101.
18. Ibid., pp. 101–6.
19. "A Nuclear Nightmare," *Time*.
20. Ibid.

21. Ibid.
22. Pringle and Spigelman, *Nuclear Barons*, pp. 426–27.
23. "Back from the Brink," *Time*, April 16, 1979.
24. Personal communication, April 1979.
25. Communication to *Time*, January 1984.
26. "Pulling the Plug," *Time*, February 13, 1984.
27. Personal communication, January 1984.

Seven The Reasons Why

1. "Three Mile Island Verdict," *Time*, August 13, 1979.
2. Ibid.
3. Ibid.
4. "Scathing Look at Nuclear Safety," *Time*, November 3, 1979.
5. John G. Kemeny et al., *Report of the President's Commission on the Accident at Three Mile Island* (Washington, D.C.: Government Printing Office, 1979), 10 vols.
6. "Scathing Look," *Time*.
7. Ibid.
8. Ibid.
9. Ibid.
10. Ibid.
11. Kemeny et al., *Report on Three Mile Island*, Vol. 10, Recommendations.
12. "Scathing Look," *Time*.
13. Ibid.
14. Pringle and Spigelman, *Nuclear Barons*, pp. 435, 436.
15. Ibid., pp. 436–43.
16. Ibid., p. 437.
17. Personal communications, August–September 1984.
18. "Taking the Cover Off a Dangerous Pressure Cooker," *Discover*, October 1984, pp. 29–32.
19. Personal communication, September 1984.
20. "Secret TMI Meetings Transcripts Show the NRC Ignores Its Responsibility," Union of Concerned Scientists, news release, June 19, 1984.
21. Pringle and Spigelman, *Nuclear Barons*, pp. 438–40.
22. "In the Matter of Metropolitan Edison Company: Aamodt Motions for Investigation of Licensee's Reports of Radioactive Releases During the Initial Days of the TMI-2 Accident and Postponement of Restart Decision Pending Resolution of this Investigation," Nuclear Regulatory Commission, Docket 50–289.
23. Union of Concerned Scientists news conference, June 19, 1984.

Eight Storm Warnings

1. Gladwin Hill, "Troubles Keep Delaying California Nuclear Plant," *The New York Times*, August 24, 1980.
2. Ibid.
3. Ibid.

4. Ibid.
5. Ibid.
6. Victor F. Zonana, "Nuclear Protesters Aim at Diablo Canyon, But PG&E Is Leaving Very Little to Chance," *The Wall Street Journal*, August 24, 1981.
7. Sara Terry, "Diablo Canyon Blockade: A-protest Leaves Both Sides Claiming Victory," *The Christian Science Monitor*, September 30, 1981.
8. Ibid.
9. "NRC Suspends Start-Up License At Diablo Canyon," *The Wall Street Journal*, November 20, 1981.
10. Ibid.
11. Ibid.
12. Thomas C. Hayes, "Diablo Canyon Reactor Starts Up Amid Protests and Industry Praise," *The New York Times*, April 30, 1984.
13. Ibid.
14. Ibid.
15. Personal communication, October 1984.
16. "1978 Economic Survey Results: Nuclear Power Generation Costs Stable, Reliability Improved," Atomic Industrial Forum News Release, May 14, 1979.
17. Charles Komanoff, *Power Propaganda: A Critique of the Atomic Industrial Forum's Nuclear and Coal Power Cost Data for 1978* (Washington, D.C.: Environmental Action Foundation, 1980).
18. Ibid.
19. Charles Komanoff, "Nuclear Industry Cost Survey Shows Coal Is Cheaper," Environmental Action Foundation News Release, June 16, 1981.
20. Ibid.
21. Charles Komanoff, *Power Plant Cost Escalation: Nuclear and Coal Capital Costs, Regulation and Economics* (New York: Komanoff Energy Associates, 1981).
22. Ibid.
23. Joseph A. Camilleri, *The State and Nuclear Power: Conflict and Control in the Western World*, (Seattle: University of Washington Press, 1984), p. 171.
24. Ibid.
25. Robert D. Hershey, Jr., "President Offers Plans for Revival of Nuclear Power," *The New York Times*, October 8, 1981.
26. Ibid.
27. Arlen J. Large, "Clinch River Project Handed Further Setback," *The Wall Street Journal*, June 8, 1984.
28. The Comptroller General, *Report to the Congress of the United States: The Clinch River Breeder Reactor—Should the Congress Continue to Fund It?*, (Washington, D.C.: U.S. General Accounting Office, May 1979).
29. *The Nuclear Almanac*, p. 410.

Nine The Crash of '84

1. "Consumers May Celebrate But a Default Could Boomerang on the Northwest," *Business Week*, July 11, 1983.
2. Ibid.
3. "If Northwest Power Network Goes Belly Up," *U.S. News & World Report*, April 4, 1983.

4. "Default Could Boomerang," *Business Week*.
5. "Whoops Woes," *Time*, May 30, 1983.
6. Ibid.
7. Ibid.
8. "Going Down," *Time*, June 27, 1983.
9. Thomas J. Lueck, "Deepening of Nuclear Woes," *The New York Times*, January 17, 1984.
10. Thomas J. Lueck, "Nuclear Cost Stirs Indiana 'Rate Shock,'" *The New York Times*, January 23, 1984.
11. Geraldine Brooks, "Cincinnati G&E's Chief Draws Fire Over Stalled Zimmer Nuclear Plant," *The Wall Street Journal*, January 18, 1984.
12. "Pulling the Nuclear Plug," *Time*, February 13, 1984.
13. "List of Troubled Reactors Grows," *The New York Times*, January 17, 1984.
14. Communication to *Time*, January 1984.
15. "Troubled Reactors," *The New York Times*.
16. Communications to *Time*, January 1984.
17. "Pulling the Plug," *Time*.
18. "Troubled Reactors," *The New York Times*.
19. Matthew L. Wald, "Lilco and Shoreham," *The New York Times*, June 8, 1984.
20. Ibid.
21. "Pulling the Plug," *Time*.
22. Communications to *Time*, January 1984.
23. "Pulling the Plug," *Time*.

Ten Energy for the Future

1. Bernard Cohen, *Before It's Too Late: A Scientist's Case for Nuclear Energy* (New York: Plenum Press, 1983), p. 120.
2. Ibid., p. 65.
3. "Pulling the Plug," *Time*.
4. George D. Russ, Jr., *Nuclear Waste Disposal: Closing the Circle* (Washington, D.C.: Atomic Industrial Forum, 1984).
5. "Pulling the Plug," *Time*.
6. Ed Bean, "Going It Alone: Duke Power Succeeds Building Nuclear Units Without Outside Help," *The Wall Street Journal*, October 17, 1984.
7. Cohen, *Before It's Too Late*, p. 31.
8. Ronald Inglehart, "The Fear of Living Dangerously; Public Attitudes Toward Nuclear Power," *Public Opinion*, February/March 1984.

Bibliography

AIF Study Group. *Nuclear Power in America's Future*. Bethesda, Md.: Atomic Industrial Forum, 1984.

An Analysis of Power Plant Construction Lead Times. Palo Alto, Cal.: Electric Power Research Institute, 2 vols., 1983.

Asimov, Isaac. *Isaac Asimov's Biographical Encyclopedia of Science and Technology*. New York: Equinox, 1972.

Behnke, Wallace B., et al. *The Technical Accomplishments of the Clinch River Breeder Reactor Plant Project*. Washington, D.C.: Atomic Industrial Forum, 1981.

Browne, Corrine, and Robert Munroe. *Time Bomb: Understanding the Threat of Nuclear Power*. New York: William Morrow and Co., 1981.

Camilleri, Joseph A. *The State and Nuclear Power: Conflict and Control in the Western World*. Seattle: University of Washington Press, 1984.

Cohen, Bernard. *Before It's Too Late: A Scientist's Case for Nuclear Energy*. New York: Plenum Press, 1983.

Comptroller General. *Report to the Congress of the United States: The Clinch River Breeder Reactor—Should the Congress Continue to Fund It?* Washington, D.C.: U.S. Government Accounting Office, 1979.

Duderstadt, James, and Chihiro Kikuchi, *Nuclear Power: Technology on Trial*. Ann Arbor, Mich.: University of Michigan Press, 1979.

Flavin, Christopher. *Nuclear Power: The Market Test*. New York: Worldwatch Institute, 1983.

Ford, Daniel. *The Cult of the Atom: The Secret Papers of the Atomic Energy Commission*. New York: Touchstone/Simon and Schuster, 1984.

Freeman, Leslie J. *Nuclear Witnesses: Insiders Speak Out*. New York: W. W. Norton, 1981.

Gray, Mike, and Ira Rosen, *The Warning*. New York: W. W. Norton & Co., 1982.

Kemeny, John G., et al., *Report of the President's Commission on the Accident at Three Mile Island*. Washington, D.C.: Government Printing Office, 10 vols., 1979.

Komanoff, Charles. *Power Plant Cost Escalation: Nuclear and Coal Capital Costs, Regulation and Economics*. New York: Komanoff Energy Associates, 1981.

Komanoff, Charles. *Power Propaganda: A Critique of the Atomic Industrial Forum's Nuclear and Coal Power Cost Data For 1978*, Washington, D.C.: Environmental Action Foundation, 1980.

Libby, Leona Marshall. *The Uranium People*. New York: Crane Russak/Charles Scribner's Sons, 1979.

Marshall, W., ed., *Nuclear Power Technology*. Oxford, England: Clarendon Press, 3 vols., 1983.

Murphy, Dervla. *Nuclear Stakes: Race to the Finish*. New York: Ticknor & Fields, 1982.

Oppenheimer, J. Robert. *Uncommon Sense*. Boston/Basel/Stuttgart: Birkhauser, 1984.

Pringle, Peter, and James Spigelman, *The Nuclear Barons*. New York: Holt, Rinehart & Winston, 1981.

Rogovin, Mitchell, et al., *Three Mile Island: A Report to the Commissioners and to the Public*. Washington, D.C.: Government Printing Office, 4 vols., 1980.

Shutdown! Nuclear Power on Trial. Summertown, Tenn.: The Book Publishing Co., 1979.

The Nuclear Almanac: Confronting the Atom in War and Peace. Reading, Mass.: Addison-Wesley Publishing Co., 1984.

TMI-2 Lessons Learned Task Force Status Report and Short-Term Recommendations. Washington, D.C.: U.S. Nuclear Regulatory Commission, 1979.

Wasserman, Harvey, and Norman Solomon, et al., *Killing Our Own*. New York: Delta, 1982.

Weber, R. L. ed., *A Random Walk in Science*. London: The Institute of Physics, 1973.

Wood, William C. *Nuclear Safety: Risks and Regulations*. Washington, D.C.: American Enterprise Institute, 1983.

Index

Aamodt, Marjorie and Norman, 131–32
Abalone Alliance, 137–38, 140
Abelson, Philip, 30
Acid rain, 10, 171
American Electric Power Company, 6, 44–45, 143
American Nuclear Energy Council, 147
Americans for Energy Independence, 71
Antinuclear groups, 4, 63, 85, 89–94, 105, 137, 145–48, 157, 163, 172, 176, 180; and Diablo Canyon plant, 138–39; impact of, 12; industry view of, 11; and Three Mile Island, 125–26, 133
Argonne National Laboratory, 32
Arthur D. Little, Inc., 158
Atomic bombs, 17, 22–23, 27
Atomic Energy Act (1946), 25, 28, 44, 47; Price-Anderson amendments to, 37, 52
Atomic Energy Commission (AEC), 14, 24–29, 32–33, 35, 37, 39, 51–58, 72, 74–75, 90, 103, 150; accidents as classified by, 70–71; Advisory Committee on Reactor Safeguards of, 59–61, 76; and Bodega cancellation, 40; and Diablo Canyon plant, 135–36; and emergency core-cooling systems, 62–68; and Fermi plant, 99; hearings by, 47–49, 64–68; Idaho test grounds of, 97–99; organizational prob-
lems of, 50; and private uranium ownership, 44, 84; and reactor technology, 41
Atomic Energy in Cosmic and Human Life, 24
Atomic Industrial Forum (AIF), 4, 6, 50, 55, 71, 104, 115, 142–44
Atoms for Peace program, 16, 28, 37

Babbit, Bruce, 123
Babcock and Wilcox, 5, 45–46, 86, 107, 125
Baker, Howard, 148–49
Barker, Hugh A., 158
Beaver Valley plant, 106
Beck, Clifford, 53–55
Beeth, Don, 8
Bendix, 49
Benedict, Manson, 71–73
Bernero, Robert M., 115, 128
Bettis laboratory, 33–34
Bodega Bay plant, 39–40, 47, 92
Bohr, Niels, 18, 29
Boiling water reactor (BWR), 35–36, 41, 72
Bonneville Power Administration, 152–53
Borch, Fred, 41–42
Breeder reactor, 30, 38
Bridenbaugh, Dale, 90
Briggs, Lyman J., 19

British Association for the Advancement of Science, 18
British Atomic Energy Authority, 96
Brookhaven National Laboratory, 52, 54–56, 59–60
Brown, Edmund G. "Jerry," Jr., 136, 138
Browns Ferry, 43–44, 58, 102–4
Bulgaria, 86
Bulletin of the Atomic Scientists, 75
Burnham, Donald, 41–42
Bush, Vannevar, 20, 22
Business and Professional People for the Public Interest, 4
Byron 1 plant, 3–4, 7, 156

Caldicott, Helen, 125
Canada, 84–85
Cancellations, 2–6, 40, 84, 160
Carnegie Institute, 20
Carter, Jimmy, 114–15, 119–20, 147
Case, Edson, 66
Cassel, Douglas, 164
Catacosinos, William, 163
China Syndrome, The, 105–6, 114
Cincinnati Gas and Electric Company, 3, 6, 8, 158–59, 164
Connecticut Light and Power Company, 161
Citizens Against Nuclear Power, 4
Clamshell Alliance, 93, 137
Clinch River Breeder Reactor Program, 148–51
Clinton Laboratories, 30
Club of Five, 85
Coal, 13, 43, 80, 157; cost of, 142–45; drawbacks and benefits of, 10, 170–72
Cohen, Bernard, 171, 178
Columbia University, 18, 20
Columbus and Southern Ohio Electric Company, 159
Comanche Peak, 13
Combustion Engineering, 5, 45–46, 86
Comey, David, 104
Commissariat à L'Énergie Atomique (CEA), 82–83
Commonwealth Edison Company, 3–4, 7, 37, 45, 58, 156
Consolidated Edison Company, 37, 51–52, 58, 90
Consumers Power Company, 7, 161–62
Conway, Richard E., 9
Cook, Donald, 45
Creitz, Walter, 111, 113–14
Cult of the Atom, The, 29, 64

Curry, Don, 110–11
Czechoslovakia, 86

Daniels reactor, 31, 32
Dayton Power and Light Company, 159
De Gaulle, Charles, 42
Der Spiegel, 125
Detroit Edison Company, 45, 99
Diablo Canyon Nuclear Power Plant, 13, 134–39, 147
Dickhoner, William, 6, 8, 164
Dietz, David, 24, 38
Dow Chemical Company, 161–62
Dresden 1 and 2, 37–38, 58
Duke Power Company, 177–78
Du Pont, 49
Duquesne Light and Power Company, 16, 36, 106

Earthquakes, 40, 106, 135–36, 139–41
Ecology Action Club, 136
Edwards, James, 147
Einstein, Albert, 18
Eisenhower, Dwight, 16, 28, 36–37
Electricité de France (EDF), 82–84, 100
Electric Power Research Institute, 146
Emergency core-cooling systems (ECCS), 46, 60, 62–68, 71
Energy consumption, 12, 150
Energy Reorganization Act (1974), 75
Energy Research and Development Administration (ERDA), 75
Enrico Fermi I reactor, 99
Environmental Action Foundation, 142–43
Environmentalists, 11–12, 39, 62–63, 85, 93, 125, 135–36, 140–41, 157, 163–64, 167
Evacuation plans, 11, 141
Experimental breeder reactor (EBR), 35
Exxon, 84

Fault-tree analysis, 72–73
Ferguson, Robert, 154
Fermi, Enrico, 18–21, 27, 29, 36
Fifth Washington Conference on Theoretical Physics, 18, 29
Finland, 85–86
Florida Power and Light, 177
Fluegge, Ronald, 90
Ford, Daniel, 28–29, 64, 104
France, 42, 79, 82–85, 92, 125–26, 176
Freedom of Information Act, 129
Frisch, Otto, 18
Fusion, 10, 167–70

Gamow, George, 24, 38
Gas-diffusion technology, 84
Gas-graphite reactors, 82, 84
General Electric Company, 5, 38, 40–46, 79, 84–86, 90, 180; and AEC contracts, 49; and Japan, 81; resignations from, 91, 94
General Public Utilities Corporation, 8, 107, 115, 121, 126, 128–29, 132
"George Shot," 27
Georgia Power, 6, 9
Geothermal power, 167–69
Germany, 19, 43, 79, 83–86, 92, 125, 176
GE Three, 94
Gilinsky, Victor, 14, 115–16, 164
Giraud, André, 83–85, 125
Gleason, George, 147
Gottlieb, Melvin, 170
Great Britain, 79, 81, 83–84, 176
Groves, Leslie R., 22, 31
Gulf, 84
Gunckel, James, 132
Gunn, Ross, 29

Hahn, Otto, 18, 20
Hanford, Washington, 22, 101
Herbein, Jack, 112, 114
Hewlett, Richard, 48
Hiroshima, 17, 22
Hitler, Adolf, 19
Hodel, Donald, 165, 179
Holifield, Chet, 55
Hosgri Fault, 135
Hosmer, Craig, 61
House Subcommittee on Government Operations, 119, 144
Houston Lighting and Power, 8
Hungary, 86
Hutchins, Robert M., 24
Hydroelectric resources, 167
Hydrogen, 113–14, 169–70
Hydrogen bomb, 27, 76

Iceland, 169
Idaho tests, 61–62, 64–65, 97–99
Illinois Tool Works, 4
Imatran Voima Oy, 86
Imperial Valley quake, 136
India, 42
Indiana, 156–58
Indian Point plants, 37, 52, 58–60, 62, 90–91
Institute for Nuclear Power Operations, 124
International Atomic Energy Agency, 47

Iodine, 97–98, 131
Iran, 88

Japan, 43, 79–82, 86, 176
Japanese Atomic Power Company (JAPCO), 81
Jersey Central Power and Light Company, 40–41, 107
Johnson, Lyndon, 44–45
Joint Committee on Atomic Energy (JCAE), 28, 48–50, 52, 55–57, 61, 68, 91, 94

Kaiser Wilhelm Institute, 18
Kansai Electric Company, 81
Kazutaka, Kikawada, 81
Kemeny Commission, 120–25
Kemeny, John, 115, 119
Kennedy, John F., 50
Kleitman, Daniel, 73
Klucsick, David, 111
Komanoff, Charles, 142–45
Kurchatov Institute, 85

Lawrence Livermore Laboratory, 10
Leeds, Steven, 138
L'Express, 125
Licensing, 3–4, 7, 12, 156, 173–74, 176; and emergency core-cooling systems, 63, 67–68
Light-water reactors, 82–83
Lilienthal, David E., 24–26
Limerick project, 159–60
Lockert, Steven, 140
Long Island Lighting Company, 6–7, 126, 162–64
Loss-of-coolant accident (LOCA), 46, 51, 53, 59, 66, 70
Lough, S. Allan, 53

McMillan, Edwin, 20
Maine Yankee plant, 106, 177
Manhattan Project, 13, 22–26, 29–31, 38, 49
Marble Hill plant, 3, 7–8, 156–58
Massachusetts Institute of Technology, 20, 71–72, 74
Media, 68, 75, 91, 93–94, 104–5; and Three Mile Island, 112–14
Meitner, Lise, 18
Meltdown, 53, 74
Merrow, Edward, 9–10
Metcalf, Pam, 137, 140
Metropolitan Edison Company, 95–96, 107–16, 118–19, 126

Meyer, Alden, 143–44
Midland plant, 7, 62, 161–62
Monsanto Chemical Company, 31
Moore, Melody, 4
Morrison, Philip, 30
Mothers for Peace, 136

Nader, Ralph, 63, 125
Nagasaki, 17, 22
National Academy of Sciences, 19, 171
National Bureau of Standards, 19
National Defense Research Committee, 20
National Environmental Policy Act (1969), 68, 161
National Reactor Testing Station, 35
Natural Resources Defense League, 63
Nautilus, 34–35, 42, 58
Naval Research Laboratory, 29–30
New England Utilities, 45
New Hampshire, 92–94
Newton, Isaac, 17–18
New York Times, The, 66, 104, 140–41
Nichols, John, 4
Nixon, Richard, 87, 180
N. S. Savannah, 38
Nuclear Analysis Center, 124
Nuclear Information and Resources Services, 148
Nuclear Regulatory Commission (NRC), 9, 14, 75–76, 91, 93, 145–46, 161, 163–64, 173, 175; and Commonwealth Edison, 156; and Diablo Canyon plant, 135–36, 139; and licensing, 3–4, 7; and Marble Hill plant, 157; and plant accidents, 103–7; and Three Mile Island, 11–12, 33, 96, 112–33
Nuclear Waste Policy Act, 175
Nucleonics Week, 91

Oak Ridge National Laboratory, 22, 30–32, 35, 100–101
Office of Scientific Research and Development, 20
Oil, 78–80, 82, 86–88, 142–45, 150, 157, 170–72
Operator error, 109, 118–19
Operator training, 11
Oppenheimer, J. Robert, 26
Organization of Petroleum Exporting Countries (OPEC), 79, 86, 88
Orr, Robert, 157
Ottinger, Richard, 148
Oyster Creek plant, 40–41, 43–44

Pacific Gas and Electric Company, 39–40, 47, 134–35, 137–40
Palladino, Nunzio, 130, 139
Peach Bottom Nuclear Power Station, 72–73
Pennsylvania Public Service Commission, 160
Philadelphia Electric Company, 3, 159–60
Philadelphia Newspapers, Inc., 129
Pilgrim plant, 62
Plant Vogtle, 9
Plutonium, 20, 22, 25, 30, 35, 147–48
Pollard, Robert, 90–91
Pollution, 10, 80, 171–72
Pressurized water reactor (PWR), 34–36, 41, 85
Price, Harold, 59–60
Princeton University, 10, 18–19, 170
Project Independence, 87
Public Service Company of Indiana, 3, 7–8, 156–57
Public Service Company of New Hampshire, 7, 92–93, 160–61
Public trust, 115–16, 132–33, 178–79

Ramey, James T., 33
Rand Corporation, 9
Rasmussen, Norman, 71–73
Rasmussen Report, 74–75, 89, 110, 116, 171
Ray, Dixy Lee, 74
Reagan, Ronald, 13, 146, 150
Reid, Robert, 112
Reynolds, Joel, 141
Ribicoff, Abraham, 33
Rickover, Hyman, 32–34, 36–37, 42
Rittenhouse, Philip, 66
Rivera, Myra, 160
Roberts, Thomas, 129–30
Roosevelt, Franklin D., 19
Rutherford, Ernest, 18

Sachs, Alexander, 19
Saint Laurent accident, 99–100
Salomon Brothers, 158
San Andreas Fault, 40
Sandia Laboratories, 49
San Luis Obispo, 136
San Onofre plant, 13
Scenic Shoreline Preservation Conference, 136
Scherer, Robert, 6, 9, 14
Scheimann, Fred, 107–8
Schlesinger, James, 67–69, 71, 74
Schmidt, Helmut, 125
SCRAM system, 21, 101, 108
Seaborg, Glenn T., 20, 23–24, 26, 30, 32–33,

38, 46–48, 50–51, 55–56, 58–61, 67
Seabrook plant, 93–94, 137, 160–61
Selby, John D., 7, 162
Sequoyah 1 and 2, 58
Shevchenko plant, 102
Shippingport Atomic Power Station, 36–37, 41–42, 57, 62, 106, 174
Shoreham plant, 6–7, 13, 126, 162–64
Siemens AG, 85
Sierra Club, 4, 63
Sinclair, Mary, 161
SL-1 excursion, 97–99, 105
Sodium-cooled reactor, 35–36, 102
Solar power, 10, 167–68
South Africa, 84
Soviet Union, 25, 27, 85–86, 102, 105, 170
Spain, 42
Sporn, Philip, 44–45
Stokes, Charles, 140
Stone and Webster, 106
Strassmann, Fritz, 18, 20
Strauss, Lewis L., 26, 141
Submarines, 29, 31–32, 34–35, 58
Submarine thermal reactor (STR) Mark I, 34
Surry Nuclear Power Station, 72–73, 106
Sweden, 43, 85
Switzerland, 42
Szilard, Leo, 18–20

Taylor, Betsy, 148
Teller, Edward, 27, 76
Tennessee Valley Authority (TVA), 5, 24, 43, 58, 81, 143; and Browns Ferry accident, 102–4
Thomas, Charles, 31
Thomson, Meldrim, 93
Thornburge, Richard, 11, 113–14, 126, 132
Three Mile Island, 8, 11–12, 33, 95–96, 107–33, 136, 142, 163, 166, 179
Tidal power, 167–69
Time magazine, 105, 179
Tokyo Electric, 81
Tolman, R. C., 24
Trinity site, 22
Trojan plant, 177
Truman, Harry S., 24–25
Turnkey projects, 43, 45
Twenty Thousand Leagues Under the Sea, 34

Union Carbide, 49
Union of Concerned Scientists, 28, 63–64, 104, 115, 129–30, 133

United Illuminating Company, 161
United Nations, 37, 47
U.S. Army, 22
U.S. Bureau of Mines, 34
U.S. Committee for Energy Awareness, 6
U.S. Geological Survey, 135, 175
U.S. Navy, 29–34, 42
University of California, 20, 26, 49
University of Chicago, 18, 20–21, 24, 29, 36, 49
University of Michigan, 178
Uranium, 18–19, 22, 25, 30, 34, 42, 66, 85, 169; private ownerships of, 44, 84
Utah, 49n.
Utility companies, 42, 44, 47, 63, 152
U-235, 20

Verne, Jules, 34

Wall Street Journal, The, 137
Walske, Carl, 4–6, 115, 123, 142, 174–76
WASH-740, 52–55, 59–61, 110
WASH-1400. *See* Rasmussen Report.
Washington Post, The, 66
Washington Public Power Supply System (WPPSS), 152–55
Waste, 128, 174–75
Weaver, Charles, 52
Weil, George, 21
Weinberg, Alvin M., 32, 51
Weiss, Ellyn R., 15, 130, 133
Westinghouse Electric Corporation, 5, 33, 36, 38, 41–46, 52, 79, 84–86, 90, 180; and AEC contracts, 49; and Americans for Energy Independence, 71; and Japan, 81
Wheeler, John A., 18
White, W. S., Jr., 6
Whiting, George, 137
Whyl protest, 92
Wicher, Jane, 4
Wigner, Eugene, 19
William H. Zimmer plant, 3, 159
Williams, Al, 155
Windpower, 10, 167–69
Windscale accident, 96–97

Yankee Atomic Electric Company, 5, 177
Yoshishige, Ashihara, 81

Zewe, Bill, 108, 110
Zinn, Walter, 30, 35
Zircaloy, 35, 36
Zirconium, 35, 66, 109